SUFFRAGETTES IN

the PURPLE WHITE & GREEN

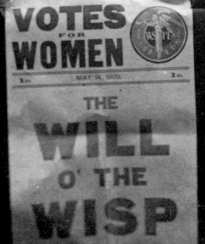

SUFFRAGETTES IN

the PURPLE WHITE & GREEN

LONDON 1906-14

DIANE ATKINSON

museum of LONDON

ACKNOWLEDGEMENTS

I would like to thank Krista Cowman, Valerie Cumming and Margaret Meyer for their questions and comments on the manuscript; Nichola Johnson and Geoffrey Toms for their unstinting support; Michael Holroyd for the story of a suffragette at George Bernard Shaw's funeral in 1950; Lisa Tickner for her excellent work on the iconography of the suffrage movement; and all my Museum of London colleagues who have generously conveyed their enjoyment of this exhibition and book.
My husband Patrick Hughes has maintained an unflagging interest in the catalogue, the exhibition and all matters suffragette above and beyond the call of marital duty.

Diane Atkinson, January 1992

Catalogue production

Editorial
Cathy Jaskowiak,
Judy Walker,
Margaret Meyer

Indexer
Margaret Christie

Design
Sally Fentiman

Photography
Torla Evans

Set in Gill Sans
Filmset, originated and
printed in England by
BAS Printers Limited,
Over Wallop, Hampshire

ISBN 0 904818 53 5

British Library Cataloguing-in-Publication Data
A CIP catalogue record for this book is available from the British Library.

Copyright © Museum of London 1992
First published 1992

CONTENTS

'Deeds Not Words'   7

The Purple, White & Green   15
Suffragette entrepreneurs and canny businessmen   15
Fashion and politics   19
The 'suffragette uniform'   23
'Spoilt for choice'   25

The Woman's Press   31
156 Charing Cross Road   34
WSPU shops in London, 1907–14   49

Endpiece   51

List of Exhibits   59

Bibliography   122

Index   130

(Front cover) *'Rise Up Women!', London procession, October 1908*
(Frontispiece) *The 'Women's Exhibition and Sale of Work in the*
Colours', Princes' Skating Rink, Knightsbridge, London, May 1909
'No effort has been spared to make the catalogue as complete and as
interesting as possible' (Votes For Women)

**Numbers in brackets after a
caption are the exhibit numbers of
objects in the exhibition**

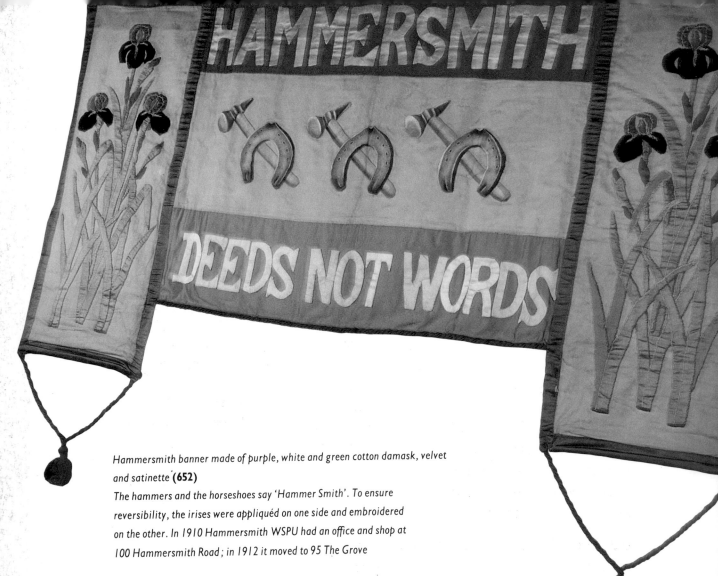

Hammersmith banner made of purple, white and green cotton damask, velvet and satinette **(652)**

The hammers and the horseshoes say 'Hammer Smith'. To ensure reversibility, the irises were appliquéd on one side and embroidered on the other. In 1910 Hammersmith WSPU had an office and shop at 100 Hammersmith Road; in 1912 it moved to 95 The Grove

'DEEDS NOT WORDS'

In October 1903 a new organisation, the Women's Social and Political Union (the WSPU), joined the 40-year-old British women's suffrage campaign. Founded in Manchester by the Pankhurst family, its style is best described by its motto: 'Deeds Not Words.'

The Pankhursts were well known politically. Dr Richard Pankhurst, known as 'The Red Doctor', and his wife Emmeline campaigned for women's rights and various radical causes until Dr Pankhurst's death in 1898. Their houses in Lancashire and London were political salons where Annie Besant, William Morris and Tom Mann (a leading trade unionist) were frequent visitors. As young children, the two eldest Pankhurst daughters, Christabel and Sylvia, accompanied their parents while canvassing and collected money at political meetings.

At the turn of the century, two-thirds of adult men in the United Kingdom could vote in parliamentary elections. Along with convicts, inmates of lunatic asylums and workhouses and the poorest men, women could not, and as a result their interests were inadequately represented in parliament.

1903

Mrs Pankhurst founds the WSPU at her home in Nelson Street, Manchester.

(Left) *The injustice of the exclusion of women from the franchise is underlined in this poster, c. 1912* **(306)**
The male gentry, agricultural labourers and factory-workers had been granted the vote during the 19th century. However, worthy women such as mothers, academics, nurses, the legally qualified, civic dignitaries, artists and myriad others had not been granted equal citizenship with men

The existing women's suffrage campaign was organised by ladylike, low-key and law-abiding 'suffragists' who included men and women. In the early 1900s their work was co-ordinated by the National Union of Women's Suffrage Societies (NUWSS), a federation of societies led by Mrs Millicent Garrett Fawcett. The campaign had achieved no progress on winning the vote for women.

1904

**[May]
Mrs Pankhurst holds a meeting outside the Houses of Parliament in protest at the 'talking-out' of a women's suffrage bill.**

Emmeline Pankhurst (1858–1928), honorary secretary
By 1913 she had served four prison sentences for charges ranging from breaking a window at 10 Downing Street to conspiracy to incite riot. In 1909 she completed a lecture tour of the United States and Canada

(Right) Adela Pankhurst (1885–1961), salaried organiser, formerly an elementary school teacher
She travelled all over the country and was arrested and imprisoned several times, being one of the first hunger-strikers. Her health broke down in 1912, and she became a gardener. Two years later she went to live in Melbourne, Australia

Mrs Pankhurst and her three daughters and their supporters determined on a new approach which was high-profile, daring and civilly disobedient. In addition to lobbying members of parliament, collecting petitions and garden party and drawing-room meetings, the WSPU included more militant tactics, such as heckling at political meetings, in their repertoire. The *Daily Mail* condescendingly nicknamed the Pankhursts' movement the 'suffragettes' in the spring of 1906. The WSPU proudly accepted the name.

First militant incident at Free Trade Hall, Manchester. Christabel Pankhurst and Annie Kenney arrested.

Sylvia Pankhurst (1882–1960), designer to the WSPU
In 1906 she gave up her studies at the Royal College of Art to work full time for the suffragette campaign, and was largely responsible for the WSPU's corporate image. Sylvia served numerous prison sentences and went on hunger, thirst and sleep strikes in protest at the government's treatment of suffragette prisoners. In the latter phase of the campaign she devoted herself especially to the plight of working-class women and built the WSPU's presence in the East End of London

Christabel Pankhurst (1880–1958), organising secretary, and later editor of The Suffragette *newspaper, inventor of the WSPU's militant tactics and a 'brilliant and popular speaker'*
She won a prize for international law in 1905, a year before she had completed her degree. In all, she served five prison sentences. She successfully evaded arrest in the spring of 1912, escaping into a self-imposed exile in Paris until the outbreak of the First World War

1906

[January] Liberals win a landslide election victory.

[Summer] The WSPU decides to fight the Liberals at all by-elections until women are given the vote.

"THEY HAVE A CHEEK I'VE NEVER BEEN ASK.

This poster (1908) made the point that parliamentary legislation would not truly represent women's interests until politicians (members of parliament) were made accountable to their female electorate **(632)**
In the 19th century factory legislation which had restricted women's working lives became law without any reference to the women themselves

These items, which belonged to Mrs Pankhurst, and the other mementoes which appear in this book, were collected in the 1920s and 1930s by the Suffragette Fellowship, whose aim was to 'perpetuate the memory of the pioneers and outstanding events connected with . . . women's emancipation and especially with the militant suffrage movement of 1905–1914'
Collar embroidered by Mrs Pankhurst **(245)**
Purple ostrich feather worn in Mrs Pankhurst's hat at the 'Rush the House [of Commons]' deputation, 13 October 1908 **(243)**
Mrs Pankhurst's black leather shoe, decorated with beads **(244)**

The moderate and militant wings of the suffrage movement shared a common goal:

> To secure for women the parliamentary vote as it is or may be granted to men; to use the power thus obtained to establish the quality of rights and opportunities between the sexes and to promote the social and industrial well-being of the community.

The purpose of this book is to describe and evaluate an unstudied aspect of the WSPU's campaign – the designing and selling, latterly called merchandising and marketing, of the Union's political message. The exhibition which this catalogue accompanies is devoted to the story of these activities in London. This is not to say that the provinces were uninvolved in or unaffected by the suffragettes' imaginative and innovative selling of their cause.

1906

[October] Arrest of ten WSPU members at the House of Commons.

Laurence Housman (1865–1959) edited this anti-Anti-Suffrage Alphabet Book of stencilled pictures and verses in 1911 **(60)**
He was a well-known book illustrator and writer, and a prominent member of the Men's League for Women's Suffrage

Bronze bust of Mrs Pankhurst made in 1912 from a model worked in Holloway Gaol by Miss Alice Morgan Wright **(242)**

(Left) *Mr Frederick Pethick-Lawrence (1871–1961)*
(Right) *Mrs Emmeline Pethick-Lawrence (1867–1954)*

1906

[February] First Women's Parliament at Caxton Hall, London. Sixty women are arrested at a demonstration at the House of Commons.

By the autumn of 1906 the WSPU had established its national headquarters at No. 4 Clement's Inn, The Strand, London. Its leaders, including the business managers Mr and Mrs Pethick-Lawrence, launched a series of financial and propaganda initiatives to fill the Union's 'war chest'. Frederick William Lawrence and Emmeline Pethick had married in 1901 and joined their surnames as a symbol of their progressive views. She was a social reformer who had founded a working girls' club with holiday hostels for members and their families, and opened a co-operative dressmaking establishment with the innovations of an eight-hour day, a paid annual holiday and a minimum weekly wage. At the time of their marriage, he was a barrister and editor of the London evening newspaper, the *Echo*. They were a formidable pair – talented and totally committed to the cause of women's suffrage.

There was no better team than the Pankhursts and the Pethick-Lawrences to recruit volunteers and raise the money needed to maintain a nationwide campaign. Unquestioning loyalty, obedience and single-mindedness were the prerequisites of membership. Mrs Pankhurst and Christabel (who held a first-class law degree but whose sex barred her from the legal profession) were both charismatic leaders. They did not tolerate those who disagreed with their policies and methods, and rejected the idea of a formally drawn constitution and democratic principles. Policy was made by the Pankhursts, fundraising was handled by the Pethick-Lawrences, and merchandising ideas were developed by the membership and a multitude of sympathisers and businesses.

Women of all ages and backgrounds joined the WSPU and worked to achieve its aims. As evidenced by the photographs in this book, we know most about the upper-class and middle-class suffragettes who appeared, fashionably dressed, at the London bazaars and processions. However, it would be wrong to assume that the comparatively small amount of photographic evidence of working-class women's involvement means that they played little part in the political or merchandising campaigns. Because of the circumstances of their lives, their domestic duties and full-time employment, not much time was left for the kind of highly visible participation captured in these photographs.

Because no membership roll was kept, for security reasons, it is difficult to present a picture of a 'typical' suffragette. However, subscription lists in the annual reports identified members' donations and marital status. Frequently members were unmarried, and surviving photographs show mostly young women. These young, middle-class women had money to spend, fewer domestic responsibilities and the time to involve themselves wholeheartedly in a political campaign which had the enormous appeal of being daring, stylish, highly visible, exciting and active.

1907

[September] Three senior members leave the WSPU – they form the Women's Freedom League, also militant.

Jessie Kenney (on the right) was Mrs Pethick-Lawrence's private secretary In her office 'plans for pestering Cabinet Ministers were laid and the most diversified measures were taken'

1907

[October] The WSPU newspaper *Votes For Women* is founded.

[Women in Finland given the vote.]

VOTES FOR WOMEN

'Votes For Women' silk scarf **(232)**
'The beauty of the scarf is not its only merit for it washes, the colours, like the principles of the Union, being fast'

Rosette badges **(208, 210)**
'Wear the colours as a duty and a privilege. Never be seen without your badge.' The initials 'E.P.' stand for Emmeline Pankhurst

THE PURPLE, WHITE & GREEN

Suffragette entrepreneurs and canny businessmen

Existing black-and-white suffragette photographs are perhaps misleading: if colour photographs were available, our abiding impression of the WSPU movement would be of a disciplined riot of colour. The purple, white and green scheme was devised by Mrs Pethick-Lawrence, treasurer and co-editor of the suffragettes' weekly newspaper *Votes For Women*. In the spring of 1908 she explained the tricolour's symbolism:

> Purple as everyone knows is the royal colour. It stands for the royal blood that flows in the veins of every suffragette, the instinct of freedom and dignity . . . white stands for purity in private and public life . . . green is the colour of hope and the emblem of spring.

Editorials in *Votes For Women* stressed the importance of wearing the colours:

> The colours enable us to make that appeal to the eye which is so irresistible. The result of our processions is that this movement becomes identified in the mind of the onlooker with colour, gay sound, movement, beauty.

Fashion and politics was a powerful new cocktail so far untried. Suffragettes were encouraged to wear the colours at all times, especially at the large demonstrations in London.

White linen handkerchief with a purple and green border **(230)**; *white cotton handkerchief embroidered with the figure of a suffragette holding a placard saying 'Votes For Women'* **(231)**

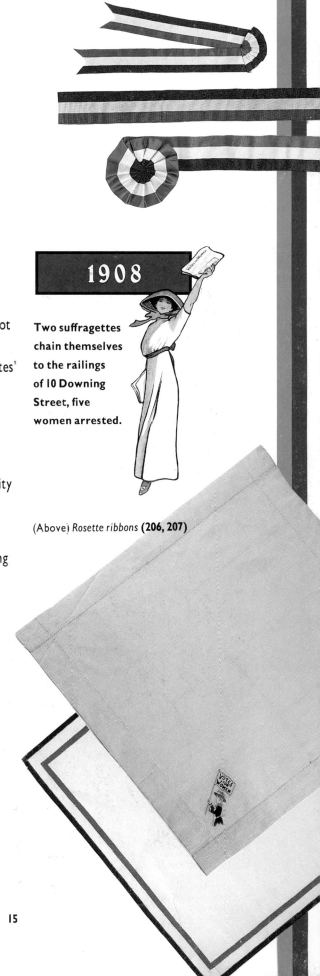

1908

Two suffragettes chain themselves to the railings of 10 Downing Street, five women arrested.

(Above) *Rosette ribbons* **(206, 207)**

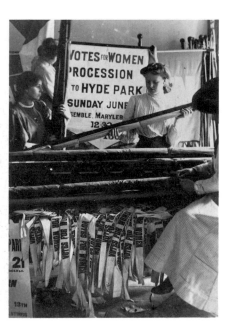

1908

'Trojan Horse'
incident –
suffragettes try
to gain entrance
to the House of
Commons hidden
in a furniture van.

'Women's Sunday' on 21 June 1908 was the WSPU's first 'monster meeting' which brought suffragettes from all over the United Kingdom to march in seven processions through the capital, culminating in a rally in Hyde Park. It was the first occasion when the colour scheme was presented to the British public. Participation in public events such as processions and rallies, let alone making far-reaching political demands, was considered by most people 'unwomanly' and 'unsexing'. Nineteenth-century domestic ideology had divided the world into two spheres, the private and the public: a woman's place was designated as 'The Home'. Suffragette activities of any nature challenged this still widely held belief. Opprobrium was rightly anticipated by the WSPU's leaders and, to try to neutralise it, conventional femininity in dress and behaviour were encouraged in the early years of the campaign.

For 'Women's Sunday', Mrs Pethick-Lawrence urged members to:

> Be guided by the colours in your choice of dress . . . we have seven hundred banners in purple, white and green. The effect will be very much lost unless the colours are carried out in the dress of every woman in the ranks. White or cream tussore should if possible be the dominant colour; the purple and green should be introduced where other colour is necessary . . . You may think that this is a small and trivial matter but there is no service that can be considered as small or trivial in this movement. I wish I could impress upon every mind as deeply as I feel myself the importance of popularising the colours in every way open to us. If every individual woman in this union would do her part, the colours would become the reigning fashion. And strange as it may seem, nothing would so help to popularise the WSPU . . . now everyone has simply got to see to it that everywhere our colours may be in evidence.

Preparing banners for 'Women's Sunday', 21 June 1908

CHORUS OF THE PURPLE, WHITE AND GREEN MARCH.

Hark to the fife ! Hark to the drum !
W.S.P.U.
Who will obey the call and come ?
W.S.P.U.
Purple a-flutter with White and Green,
W.S.P.U.
What do the tricolour standards mean ?
W.S.P.U.

Purple stands for the loyal heart,
Loyal to cause and King ;
White for Purity, **Green** for hope,
Bright hopes of Spring.

March and fight through the long, long night
That our children be brave and free !
March and fight for our one common right,
Citizens to be !

1908

Cabinet ministers playing golf are ambushed by suffragettes who have hidden in bushes on the course.

The words and music of 'The Purple, White and Green March' were written for the procession of 18 June 1910 by Mr Reginald Potts

'Women's Sunday'
'The dignity, the grace, the beauty, the courage of the processionists carried conviction everywhere. Scoffers were converted. Some who had evidently come to jeer stayed to cheer. . . The crying out of words of encouragement must have been very gratifying to those among the processionists who have withstood harshness and insults' (Daily News)

'Votes For Women' buttons **(205)**
(Loan item from the Fawcett Library, City of London Polytechnic)

1908

[April] **Prime Minister Henry Campbell-Bannerman dies and is replaced by Henry H. Asquith, who strongly opposes women's suffrage.**

The members followed these instructions and made a vivid impression on those who watched the thousands of women march through London to Hyde Park. *The Times* reporter noted:

> At the head of each procession was carried a flag of purple, white and green . . . and after that the 'regimental colours' so to speak – a beautiful silk banner also in purple, white and green with artistic embroidery and symbolical devices . . . Each group . . . marched under a banner of its own and every woman walking in the procession wore the purple, white and green either in the favours pinned to the breast, or in the trimmings of the hat, in belt ribbons or in the shoulder sashes. Many of the ladies wore costumes designed in an arrangement of purple, white and green, white frocks being the general wear . . . The men, of whom there were several assisting the stewards, had them as ties, as badges or the bands around Panama or boating hats. Street hawkers were offering them in rosettes for the button holes and small bouquets of pansies, with a spray of lily of the valley and some fern.

This was the first of many such occasions when flower-sellers, aware of the rewards from a captive audience, positioned themselves along the procession routes, which were publicised well in advance.

Votes For Women, May 1910

WHERE TO SHOP.

VOTES FOR WOMEN DIRECTORY,

Bootmakers.

Debenham & Freebody	Shoolbred's
Derry & Toms	Spiers & Pond's
Lilley & Skinner	Thos. Wallis & Co.
London Shoe Company	Whiteley's
Peter Robinson	William Owen

Cycle Makers.

Marston Cycle Co.	Palmer Tyre Co.

Dealers in Antiques.

Miss May Stuart Elliott	Mrs. Trevor.

Dentists.

A. F. Green	Chadwick Brown

Drapers and Hosiers.

Debenham & Freebody	Shoolbred's
Derry & Toms	Spiers & Pond's
John Barker	Thos. Wallis & Co.
John Lindsay	Tudor Bros.
Peter Robinson	Whiteley's
Selfridge's	William Owen

Dressmakers.

Amy Kotzé	Peter Robinson
Chas. Lee & Sons	Rebecca Gordon
Debenham & Freebody	Selfridge's
Derry & Toms	Shoolbred's
Forma	Thelma
John Barker	Thos. Wallis & Co.
Madame Vernon	Violetta
Maud Barham	Whiteley's
Mora Puckle	William Owen

Dyers and Dry Cleaners.

Brand & Mollison	E. Day & Co.
Clark & Co.	

Florists, &c.

A. Cheesley	Shearn's
Derry & Toms	Spiers & Pond's
Mrs. Stickland	

Furnishers.

Derry & Toms	Shoolbred's
John Barker	Spiers & Pond's
Selfridge's	William Owen

Hairdressers.

Ludicke	Ray & Sons

Health Foods.

Allinson's Bread	Shearn's
Bragg's Charcoal Biscuits	Wallace Food
Savage's Nuts	

Fashion and politics

Businesses quickly turned the suffragette colour scheme to their advantage. Individual entrepreneurs (some of them suffragettes), small businesses and major stores such as Peter Robinson and Liberty, made or stocked tricolour clothes and accessories, all with the purchasing power of middle-class suffragettes in mind. They informed WSPU headquarters of their stock and took advertising space in *Votes For Women*. At its height the paper sold 40,000 copies a week and had an average weekly readership of 160,000.

The WSPU was anxious that members should patronise these firms. The intentions behind the regular fashion feature in *Votes For Women*, called 'Concerning Dress', were obvious. A broad discussion of the season's popular fashions quickly developed into strong hints about suitable clothes for particular WSPU events. Whether the activity was an outdoor procession, rally, indoor meeting or breakfast party to welcome released prisoners, the column always wrote favourably about purple, white and green fashion and whoever made or sold such items. Suffragette entrepreneurs and sympathisers received especially warm praise and close attention. In October 1908, readers were reminded:

> There are one or two occasions already on the programme when it will be essential to the general effect that all members of the Union shall wear full dress uniform, ie, the white frock with regalia and colours. So we must see to it that we have at least one white frock in our winter wardrobe. At the meeting in the Albert Hall on October 29th every suffragette shall be distinguished at a glance by her white uniform. . . For events of lesser importance and for outdoor processions we shall have to fall back upon those shades of purple and green which tone with the belts and regalia and badge in the tricolour.

The 'suffragette look' worn by Miss Norah Balls

1908

[30 June] Mary Leigh and Edith New become the first suffragette window-smashers.

[Women in Norway given the vote.]

Then came the endorsements:

> One cannot walk down Bond Street and the neighbourhood without being struck by the fact that our colours are evidently going to be the leading shades in the autumn and winter months. Almost every shop window is showing purple hats and green hats, purple ties and green ties, purple gowns and green gowns in endless variety. Mrs Oliver was the first of the Bond Street dressmakers to realise the value of *Votes For Women* as an advertising medium, and her prices, considering the neighbourhood, are exceedingly moderate. Her address is 115 Bond Street. Another dressmaker who takes a keen interest in the women's fight for the vote is Elspeth Phelps of 49 South Molton Street. Miss Phelps who is an ardent suffragette has some exquisite models on view and one of those shown to our representative was admirably adapted to the purple, white and green; a directoire gown which would be made in a dark shade of purple cloth with dainty yoke and tucked sleeves of white net, edged with a very narrow band of green silk; or the colours might be reversed.

If WSPU members were in any doubt about the merits of combining fashion, consumerism and politics, 'all good suffragists must realise that in giving their custom to the suffragists advertising in *Votes For Women* they are very materially helping the cause'.

In April 1909, an article called 'Where Dresses Can Be Bought in the Colours' gave detailed advice on this matter. William Owen, of Westbourne Grove, stocked 'long purple serge coats whose collars and cuffs were trimmed in green and bordered with white'. Peter Robinson, of Oxford Street, sold 'dress materials, blouses, princess dresses, costumes and gauze scarves for motoring' in the colours. The millinery department of Derry and Toms, Kensington, stocked hats, flowers and ribbons, and their footwear department had tricolour kid shoes.

1908

[13 October] 'Rush' on the House of Commons: WSPU leaders and more than 30 other members arrested.

Advertisements in Votes For Women, *March and December 1909*

The 'suffragette look'
Front row, middle to right: *Mary Gawthorpe (in dark dress)*, *Christabel Pankhurst*, *Mrs Pethick-Lawrence* and *Annie Kenney*
Back row, extreme left: *Dorothy Pethick (sister of Mrs Pethick-Lawrence)*, far right: *Jessie Kenney*

1908

Politicians heckled by suffragettes at meetings all over the United Kingdom.

[**Women in Victoria, Australia, given the vote.**]

The summer sales of 1909 reveal more businesses identifying suffragettes as important customers. Apparently, 'almost every draper of any standing now stocks dresses, hats, ties, hosiery, etc in the purple, white and green'. Lilley and Skinner shoe shops dressed their windows in WSPU colours and added a new line – 'bedroom slippers in velvet and quilted satin specially dyed in the colours'. The London Shoe Company sold purple, white and green shoes, and Jaeger's, of Regent Street, offered to make up its goods (specifically clothing) in the colours. Derry and Toms stocked tricolour underwear in their lingerie department.

Evidence suggests that takings rose in the weeks before a major rally or procession in London, but that leading stores and smaller shops all over the capital kept a regular stock of purple, white and green items. Further, we might assume that bolder suffragettes wore the tricolour every day, not only at special events.

West Ham banner made of purple, white and green silk, wool and velvet, bearing Sylvia Pankhurst's 'angel' design (647)

1909

[Spring] Seventy-five women now on the WSPU payroll. Branches open throughout the country.

The 'suffragette uniform' is here being worn by Daisy Dugdale, standard-bearer of the procession, welcoming Mrs Pankhurst and her daughter Christabel on their release from Holloway Gaol, 19 December 1908

Some suffragettes even wore the colours at their weddings. In August 1909, Miss Ruth Robson married Reverend T. Dring at Bowes Park in East London. According to a report in *Votes For Women*:

> The colours were greatly in evidence, appearing in the bride's bouquet, the wedding favours and button-holes, while the bride's 'going-away' dress was in purple, white and green. Members of the local Union dressed in the colours, wearing the regalia, and carrying banners formed a guard of honour at the station and gave the bride and groom a hearty send-off.

The 'suffragette uniform'

For special occasions such as the breakfast parties welcoming suffragette prisoners freed from Holloway Gaol and prisons all over the country, WSPU members were given explicit instructions to wear 'the uniform'. The reception planned for the release of Mrs Pankhurst and her daughter Christabel from Holloway in December 1908 was publicised well in advance:

> We heartily urge all those who can do so to make a special effort to wear the uniform. It will consist of a short skirt of purple or green, a white golf jersey and a simple hat of purple or green. The regalia [sash] will be worn over the right shoulder and will be fastened under the left arm.

1909

[29 June] Whitehall office windows smashed by suffragettes after Asquith consistently refuses to see their deputations. The 14 window-smashers serve one month in Holloway Gaol.

Large rectangular cotton banner **(650)**
Suffragette propagandists used puns such as 'Ask With/Asquith' on banners, postcards and posters

Rose Lamartine Yates and her son Paul, born in 1908
'A convincing outdoor and indoor speaker', Rose was the honorary organising secretary of Wimbledon WSPU. In 1909 she was charged with obstruction while on a deputation and served a month in prison

(Above) Votes For Women, *November 1908*

(Right) Votes For Women, *June 1911*

1909

[July] First suffragette hunger-strike. Suffragette sculptor Marjorie Wallace Dunlop refuses to eat in protest at treatment of suffragettes in prison. All hunger-strikers released early.

While it is not certain who designed or manufactured the uniform, it is likely that the idea was suggested by staff and volunteers at the Clement's Inn headquarters.

Even though the WSPU offered a large assortment of purple, white and green novelties such as badges and games, its selection and stock of clothing was limited. Other than silk scarves, a couple of designs for muslin blouses and the 'suffragette uniform', evidence suggests that the leadership preferred that individuals and store buyers initiate and manufacture fashions and accessories, and did not engage in joint business ventures.

The strength of the manufacturers' and retailers' response to the WSPU's colour scheme suggests that it succeeded in recruiting large numbers of women into the organisation. The suffragettes were the fastest-growing group in the women's suffrage movement in the six years before the start of the First World War; they may or may not have been the biggest grouping, but they were the most active and the most visible. So successful was the tricolour scheme that the rival suffragists of Mrs Garrett Fawcett's organisation adopted their own red, white and green, the Actresses' Franchise League pink, green and white and an offshoot of the WSPU, the Women's Freedom League, wore green, white and gold.

In addition to clothes and accessories, there were other indications of the colour scheme's popularity – pavements were frequently chalked with announcements of meetings and special events in purple, white and green, and posters and handbills were sometimes printed in the colours.

Votes For Women, *June 1911*

Charming Hats for the June 17 Demonstration. Special Display at **DERRY & TOMS,** KENSINGTON HIGH ST., LONDON, W.

For the Great Demonstration, June 17th.

PETER ROBINSON REGENT ST

'Spoilt for choice'

Female entrepreneurs, including suffragettes and suffragette sympathisers, produced an impressive range of items in purple, white and green, often bearing the slogan 'Votes For Women'. Other supporters provided sundry services with direct appeal to WSPU members.

In *Votes For Women*, Roberta Mills of Brixton declared that there was 'Nothing like Leather for Suffragettes Wear'. 'Suffragette milliner' Clara Strong offered hats and toques trimmed in the 'Colours of the Union'. Dorothy Eckford of Bognor, Sussex, sold sweet pea seeds by mail order, specialising in the suffragette colours. Mrs Courtenay Wallis of Westbourne Grove advertised hatpins in the colours, and the artist Edith Downing, a leading member of the Chelsea WSPU, made statuettes of Christabel Pankhurst and Annie Kenney (the first suffragettes to be arrested) for five guineas and two guineas respectively. The Home Restaurant in the City of London provided 'dainty luncheons and afternoon teas and home-made cakes iced in the colours'. Suffragette toilet soap, 'Once Tried Always Used', was made in Halifax, and there was an advertisement 'Vote for Allinson's Wholemeal Bread'. There were even battery-operated brooches which flashed 'Votes For Women'.

1909

A group of suffragettes row across the moat of Lympne Castle in Kent, scale the wall and shout slogans at Prime Minister Asquith, who is dining with his family.

(Below) Votes For Women, *February 1909*

LARA STRONG, Suffragette Millin
Toques (ready to wear), trimmed in the Colours of the
Hand-made, trimmed to order, from 5/11.
ection always in stock.   Orders by post receive prom
, ELSPETH ROAD, LAVENDER HILL, S

*The Women's Coronation
Procession, 17 June 1911*

Hilda Dallas (1878–1958) designed several posters and this Christmas card for the WSPU **(235)**

1909

[September] Force-feeding of hunger-striking suffragettes begins.

Handbill advertising the Women's Coronation Procession **(548)**

VOTES FOR WOMEN
Women's Coronation
PROCESSION
(Five miles long)
Saturday, June 17th,
START **5.30** P.M.
Route via:—TRAFALGAR SQUARE, PALL MALL, PICCADILLY, KNIGHTSBRIDGE.
70 BANDS!
1,000 BANNERS!

Services as well as goods were provided by suffragette entrepreneurs. 'Art photographer' Annie Bell offered special terms to WSPU members; Grace Jones of Camden Town 'inexpensively and artistically decorated rooms' for suffragettes; the slogan for the Beaconsfield Laundry in Kilburn was 'Votes For Women and a Good Laundry'; Miss Rosa Leo, who taught voice classes and public speaking, boasted of 'great success with members of the WSPU'; and a Suffragette Self-Defence Club operated twice a week from a house in Kensington where ju-jitsu lessons were given to suffragettes who 'wish to repel hooligan attacks'.

The Women's Coronation Procession of 17 June 1911 offered more scope for women entrepreneurs to use their merchandising and marketing skills. The WSPU arranged a march in London of some 60,000 women a week before the coronation of King George V. Many new items were advertised in *Votes For Women* in the weeks preceding the event. Annette Jay of London, a milliner and corsetière, wished 'to draw the attention of the WSPU to the fact that they are making a speciality of Procession Hats and Toques in the Colours of the Union. They also wish to point out that the Spirella Corsets, the boning of which is unbreakable and rust-proof, are highly recommended owing to their comfort to those marching and speaking.' Roberta Mills advertised her 'Emmeline Bag' and 'Christabel Shopping Bag'.

Interesting Items fr and some in the

Handbags.
Suffrage Dorothy Bags of soft kid, draw-cords with White ground and Purple and Green leather stripes. Price - **3/6**
Crocodile Handbags with outside pocket, in Light Brown, Dark Brown, and Green Skin. Price - **7/6**
Fitted Handbag of Beaver Calf in various colours. A most handy outdoor companion. Price - **14/6**

Ribbons.
Strong Corded Ribbon in

The Women's Tea Company, which was owned by the Gibbons sisters, offered to pack tea, coffee, cocoa and chocolates 'of the best quality at moderate prices' in the colours. Special terms were offered to suffragette shops and bazaars, and jobs as agents for their business were advertised in *Votes For Women*. Eighteen months previously, the sales department of The Woman's Press responded to the many requests for 'Votes For Women' tea, packaging it with a logo designed by Sylvia Pankhurst. The Gibbons sisters understood the potential of suffragette buyers and adapted the suffragettes' tea idea to their own range of products.

Christabel Pankhurst's near arrest on charges of conspiracy to incite violence and her self-imposed exile in Paris in the spring of 1912 led to several new items being devised, including 'Christabel Cakes', made by Miss Edith Woollan of Cricklewood. Early on in the campaign, Christabel had endorsed the 'Ivelcon Beef and Vegetable Consommé Cube':

> Dear Suffering Sister Suffragettes, our day of triumph is at hand. . . I will disclose to you my scheme for the subjection of that tyrant – man. What could be more simple than to attack him in his weakest spot, lure him on by feeding him with Ivelcon and all the other St Ivel dainties you know so well and thus make him so pleased and so satisfied that he will grant anything, especially votes. Historians of the future will write about the 'Ivelconquest of the Commons'.

Selfridge's of Oxford Street sold a large range of goods and went so far as to fly a purple, white and green flag from their own flagpole when Mrs Pankhurst was released from Holloway Gaol in the spring of 1909. Also that spring, the Elswick Cycle Company of Newcastle upon Tyne had designed 'a bicycle specially for the use of WSPU members . . . beautifully enamelled in the well-known Elswick Green, lined in the colours of the Union . . . the gearcase bearing the Medallion of Freedom [designed by Sylvia Pankhurst], price ten guineas'.

Votes For Women, March 1910

1909

Cabinet ministers 'pestered' by suffragettes all over the country.

From the spring of 1909 the WSPU had its own Women's Band and a Junior Band **(222)**

The Suffragette, September 1913

1909

Conciliation Committee formed to draft a women's suffrage bill – the Conciliation Bill. (Between 1910 and 1912 three such bills are drafted and debated, and all fail.)

Fuelled by growing anger and frustration at the Liberal government's failure to legislate on women's suffrage, the Pankhurst-led WSPU grew more militant. Suffragettes began harrassing politicians and attacking private and commercial property. Their aim was to force the government to act. Nation-wide window-smashing and arson attacks would, they declared, win women the vote. Window-smashing by day, suffragettes were often arrested near the scene; arsonists at night, they were rarely caught. To avoid loss of life, only *unoccupied* government buildings, politicians' residences and private houses were targeted. If the attack took place at night, one of their newspapers was sometimes left behind. Suffragettes who could not condone the escalating violence left the WSPU; those who remained became even more convinced of the rightness of the new direction. For its part, the government became more entrenched and determined not to give in to the militants; the British press and public opinion turned against their cause.

Somewhat surprisingly, when the WSPU's campaign was at its most destructive (when commercial premises had their windows smashed, and houses were burnt and bombed to the ground), businesses still took advertising space in *Votes For Women* and later *The Suffragette*, albeit at a reduced level. Hostile to the tactics of the post-1911 period, some firms withdrew. A number of entrepreneurs and businesses which had manufactured fashion and beauty goods for the kind of feminine suffragette previously favoured by the leadership were unable to understand, let alone condone, the militants. For them, and indeed the majority of the British public, femininity and militancy were incompatible.

There was even no guarantee that a store which advertised in the paper would escape window-smashing. Selfridge's and Robinson and Cleaver, two regular advertisers, had their windows smashed in 1911, but continued their relationship with the WSPU. Selfridge's co-published with the Union a *Women's Suffrage Annual* and *Who's Who* in 1913 and advertised in *The Suffragette* up to the start of the First World War in August 1914. Parallel with the growing aggression of the campaign was the decision of The Woman's Press to wind down some of its merchandising and marketing operations in order to concentrate on political activities.

Given the alienation of the militant suffragettes from the public, it is remarkable that any firms continued to advertise in *The Suffragette*, the most stridently militant of the women's suffrage weeklies. 'The Busy Buyer's Guide' was a regular feature throughout 1913 and 1914 which listed all the companies supporting the suffragettes by doing business with the WSPU. Christabel Pankhurst, the editor of *The Suffragette*, strongly urged members to patronise such firms. Even as late as May 1914, when the most militant suffragettes were regarded as an army of wild women, 35 businesses were listed in the guide. These included Dunhill cigarettes, the Express Dairy and the big stores: Jaeger, Debenham and Freebody, D.H. Evans, Harvey Nichols, Swan and Edgar, and Marshall and Snelgrove. Their support was in direct contrast to the unanimous public vilification of suffragettes while on active service. One young girl handing out leaflets was set upon by a group of medical students and stripped and tarred. Angry diners at Lyons Restaurant in Piccadilly pelted suffragettes with food, crockery and cutlery. It seems perverse that firms would risk losing customers who disapproved of the WSPU's policies : these businesses must have judged that it was financially expedient to continue the relationship with suffragette shoppers who, they could argue, were not all militants.

Both the nature of the entrepreneurial activity and the merchandise itself indicate the tastes and buying preferences of the average suffragette. A love of ornament and desire to proclaim allegiances is evidenced by the wide selection of clothing in the colours, fine jewellery and inexpensive badges and brooches. The lasting image of the suffragettes is emphatically feminine, bourgeois and middle class. Sadly, we have no such visual record of their working-class sisters, whose wages could only run to postcards of their heroines, a length of ribbon and a tin badge.

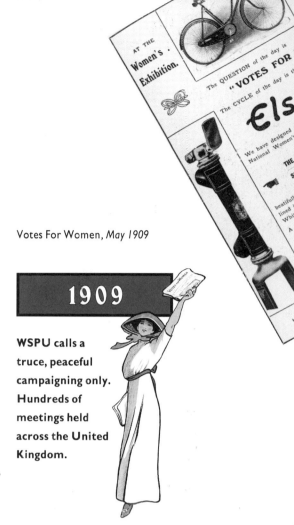

Votes For Women, *May 1909*

1909

WSPU calls a truce, peaceful campaigning only. Hundreds of meetings held across the United Kingdom.

Votes For Women, *December 1909*

In the Union Colours.

SILKUNA KNITTED SPORTS COATS.

Made exclusively for Debenham & Freebody, closely resembling real silk in appearance, perfect fitting, the cut, style, and finish of a tailor-made coat. In mauve, purple, new plum, new mole, emerald green, saxe and turquoise blue, cerise, and the combined colours of the Union are amongst the leading shades in these fashionable coats. 45 inches long.

59/6
Knitted Caps to match, 5/11
Sent on Approval.

Debenham & Freebody,
Wigmore Street, London, W.

1910

**[18 November]
'Black Friday'.
Riot outside
the House of
Commons, 120
women arrested,
many assaulted by
the police. Riots
in Parliament
Square the
following week.**

Shield-shaped silver and enamel pin **(196)** and circular enamel WSPU badge **(195)**

'This year, I have never once appeared anywhere without my badge and it has been the means of opening conversation . . . and enlightening many people on various points on which they were in doubt and in putting before them a different point of view of our whole movement from that which they get in the daily press. I have also been able to get people to subscribe to Votes For Women. I wish all our members would faithfully wear the badge.' (Mrs East, Honorary Secretary of Chiswick WSPU, 1909)

'Pank-a-Squith', the 'highly artistic Table Game that helps to spread the movement . . . PUZZLES, AMUSES, TEASES, EXCITES, SETS EVERYBODY LAUGHING' **(282)**
First available in the autumn of 1908, it concerned 'the attempt of a "Suffragette" to get from her house to the Houses of Parliament. She has to cross fifty sections and meet with all sorts of opposition'

'Panko' card game **(276)**

THE WOMAN'S PRESS

The Woman's Press was founded as the WSPU's publishing imprint and distribution house for its weekly newspaper *Votes For Women* and its books, pamphlets and colours. Salaried staff were helped by a rising number of volunteers. From the spring of 1908 The Woman's Press at 4 Clement's Inn stocked purple, white and green products and novelties such as brooches and badges, scarves, ties, hatpins, flags, the 'suffragette uniform', teasets specially manufactured with a logo designed by Sylvia Pankhurst, postcard albums and stationery. Also available were Woman's Press books and leaflets, such as *The Importance of the Vote*, *The Militant Methods of the W.S.P.U.* and *The Awakening of Women*.

From the outset Frederick Pethick-Lawrence gave priority to selling the WSPU's advertising space in *Votes For Women*. Sales of WSPU newspapers and Woman's Press publications were not only essential for spreading the suffragettes' message, but important to the Union's annual balance sheet.

Christmas was always used by The Woman's Press to boost revenue for the 'war chest' and widen support. WSPU shops around the country would stock up and dress their windows with gifts in purple, white and green or with the 'Votes For Women' slogan. There were Christmas cards, calendars and crackers, cakes iced in the colours and jewellery, as well as suffragette dolls (sometimes dressed in prison clothing) and 'Cabinet Mincemeat'. Several London manufacturers devised special board games and card games such as 'Pank-a-Squith', 'Panko', 'In and Out of Holloway Gaol', 'The Game of the Suffragette', 'Rushing the House' and 'The Ladies Puzzle'. In December 1909 Kensington WSPU advertised 'Militant Jam With Stones' or 'Stoneless Variety, the stones extracted for other purposes'.

1910

WSPU renews its truce and is optimistic about a second Conciliation Bill.

[Women in Washington State given the vote.]

At 4 Clement's Inn, July 1911

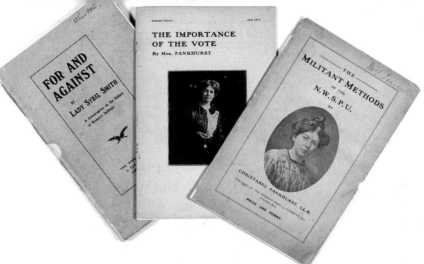

From the outset, the WSPU excelled at putting its message across, here in books and pamphlets . . .

1911

Peaceful
methods
for most of
this year.

[Women in
California given
the vote.]

. . . and in handbills

From left to right : 'The Militant Methods of the NWSPU' ; 'Is the English
Law Unjust to Women?' ; 'Some Questions Answered' ; 'What Women
Get, and What They Need' ; 'The Tactics of the Suffragettes'

Portrait button badge of Mrs Pankhurst, price one penny **(194)**
More expensive versions had purple, white and green ribbons

The WSPU shop in Reading opened in the summer of 1910
On 1 July its organiser, Miss Margesson, wrote: 'The shop is now open and reported to be very alluring. Call and see it and volunteer to help "keep" it, especially during the afternoons. The open air campaign is now in full swing; special dinner hour meetings for factory girls are being arranged, in addition to four evening weekly meetings . . . there is plenty of work for all'

1911

[April] Many suffragettes refuse to fill in their census forms.

[Autumn] No progress on Conciliation Bill.

Originally a threepenny monthly founded in October 1907, Votes For Women soon became a penny weekly sold by newsagents all over the United Kingdom

156 Charing Cross Road

The Woman's Press was so successful that in May 1910 half of its
staff of 25 left their Clement's Inn offices for premises at 156
Charing Cross Road, comprising 12 rooms, a basement and shop.
A Mrs Knight ran the office and was responsible for sales of the
colours, Woman's Press literature and weekly orders of *Votes For
Women*. Editorial work and advertisements and subscriptions for
the paper continued to be handled at Clement's Inn. By 1910 the
Press's turnover had reached £12,000 (£480,000 in 1992 values)
compared to £60 four years earlier. Its 1910 annual report
declared: 'The story of The Woman's Press constitutes a veritable
romance which would provoke to envy any business house run on
ordinary lines.' Its new central London location was only 'three
doors away from Oxford Street' and it was envisaged that it would
'attract the ordinary passer-by'. The opening ceremony on 4 May
was performed by Miss Fanny Brough, a well-known actress, and
Miss Evelyn Sharp, a best-selling novelist.

1911

**[November]
WSPU furious
over the new bill
announced by the
government to
give more votes to
men, not women.**

*Today the Centrepoint building stands on the site of The Woman's
Press, 156 Charing Cross Road*

(Far left) *Beaded glass necklace* **(203)**

1911

[21 November] **Widespread window-smashing, government and commercial properties attacked. Over 200 suffragettes arrested and sentenced to up to two months in Holloway. Public opinion alienated by the firing of churches, houses and public amenities. Golfing greens attacked with acid, letters burnt in pillar-boxes, buildings daubed with slogans.**

The Woman's Press shop, 156 Charing Cross Road
(Top) *Notice the fashion accessories top right*
(Bottom) *Notice the postcard albums on the high shelf; 'Votes For Women' tea on the floor; a satchel for selling the newspaper; and a kite on the right, doubtless in the colours*

(Below) *Ordinary playing cards printed in the suffragette way* **(286)**

Six weeks after opening business was good and many visitors, including foreign tourists 'anxious to understand the various aspects of the movement', had helped to boost the takings:

> The shop itself is a blaze of purple, white and green and the mere enumeration of the pretty and useful things for sale would fill this entire [*Votes For Women*] newspaper column. Just now [July 1910] The Woman's Press is showing some beautiful motor and other scarves in various shades of purple as well as white muslin summer blouses and among the almost unending variety of bags, belts, etc are the noticeable 'Emmeline' and 'Christabel' bags and the 'Pethick' tobacco pouch. In addition to books, pamphlets and leaflets, stationery, games, blotters, playing cards and indeed almost everything that can be produced in purple, white and green, or a combination of all three is to be found here.

1912

[5 March] Police raid WSPU headquarters. The leadership is found guilty of conspiracy to incite violence and sentenced to nine months in prison.

'Holiday campaigns' packs of postcards, pamphlets and handbills were available for members who wanted to spread the word while on their summer holiday

Advertisement for 'Panko'
On the left, Prime Minister Asquith is parodied as an old-fashioned naval caricature in flight. In contrast, on the right, Christabel Pankhurst, wearing legal, academic robes, is presented head on and in control, making the demand from which he is hurrying to escape

Half the rooms were devoted to organising the selling of *Votes For Women* throughout the United Kingdom, dispatching it abroad, and distributing other propaganda material. The newspaper was printed in London and on Thursday, which was publication day, a Mrs Tuckwell would drive the highly decorated 'press cart' rapidly round to the various pitches all over London with supplies for that day. Tuesday and Friday were 'poster parade' days, organised by Miss Laura Ainsworth, when suffragettes 'set forth carrying posters and sometimes sunshades [or umbrellas in the winter] in the colours advertising the week's newspaper. These parades attract a great deal of attention.' A common sight was the WSPU's purple, white and green Austin motor car, decorated with posters, being driven through London by the Union's chauffeuse Vera 'Jack' Holme. In 1908 at Mrs Pankhurst's suggestion the membership had donated the money for the car which was presented to Mrs Pethick-Lawrence as a tribute to her hard work.

(Above) *The* Votes For Women *parade of press carts in London during 'Votes For Women Week', July 1911*
'Outside the theatres where matinées were being given a halt was made and the Votes For Women *sold'*

(Right) *Laura Ainsworth wearing the Holloway Badge at her throat for going to prison, and on her chest the hunger-strike medal 'For Valour' She was arrested in Birmingham in 1909 for stone-throwing and force-fed while on hunger-strike in Winson Green Gaol*

1912

[**October**] **The Pethick-Lawrences are purged from the WSPU but continue to edit and publish** *Votes For Women*. **The new official headquarters, run by Mrs Pankhurst, Annie Kenney and 'General' Flora Drummond, opens at Lincoln's Inn House in Kingsway.** *The Suffragette*, **a more militant weekly paper, is launched.**

A stocking filler for Christmas **(280)**

*A 'press cart'
'Votes For Women Weeks' were
held every year to boost sales*

Paste necklace believed to have been worn by Mrs Pankhurst **(204)**

Advertisement for The Woman's Press shop
The Votes For Women clock above the shop was a familiar sight in
Charing Cross Road

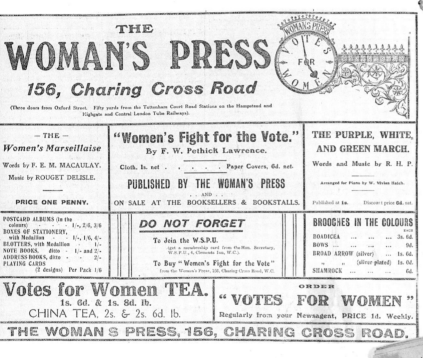

THE WOMAN'S PRESS
156, Charing Cross Road

(Three doors from Oxford Street. Fifty yards from the Tottenham Court Road Stations on the Hampstead and Highgate and Central London Tube Railways).

— THE —
Women's Marseillaise

Words by F. E. M. MACAULAY.

Music by ROUGET DELISLE.

PRICE ONE PENNY.

"Women's Fight for the Vote."
By F. W. Pethick Lawrence.

Cloth, 1s. net . . . . . . Paper Covers, 6d. net.

PUBLISHED BY THE WOMAN'S PRESS
. . AND . .
ON SALE AT THE BOOKSELLERS & BOOKSTALLS.

THE PURPLE, WHITE,
AND GREEN MARCH.

Words and Music by R. H. P.

Arranged for Piano by W. Vivian Hatch.

Published at **1s.**   Discount price **6d.** net.

POSTCARD ALBUMS (in the colours) - - 1/-, 2/6, 3/6
BOXES OF STATIONERY, with Medallion - 1/-, 1/6, 4/-
BLOTTERS, with Medallion - 1/-
NOTE BOOKS, ditto - 1/- and 2/-
ADDRESS BOOKS, ditto - 2/-
PLAYING CARDS
(2 designs) Per Pack 1/6

DO NOT FORGET

To Join the W.S.P.U.
(get a membership card from the Hon. Secretary, W.S.P.U., 4, Clements Inn, W.C.).

To Buy "Women's Fight for the Vote"
from the Woman's Press, 156, Charing Cross Road, W.C.

BROOCHES IN THE COLOURS
EACH
BOADICEA ... ... 3s. 6d.
BOWS ... ... 9d.
BROAD ARROW (silver) ... 1s. 6d.
" " (silver-plated) 1s. 0d.
SHAMROCK ... ... 6d.

Votes for Women TEA.
1s. 6d. & 1s. 8d. lb.
CHINA TEA, 2s. & 2s. 6d. lb.

ORDER
"VOTES FOR WOMEN"
Regularly from your Newsagent, PRICE 1d. Weekly.

THE WOMAN'S PRESS, 156, CHARING CROSS ROAD.

The front page of Votes For Women always carried a satirical cartoon
depicting the current political situation

VOTES FOR WOMEN
EDITED BY FREDERICK AND EMMELINE PETHICK LAWRENCE
VOL. VI. (New Series), No. 268.   FRIDAY, APRIL 25, 1913.   Price 1d. Weekly

YIELDING TO FORCE

In other rooms at Charing Cross Road posters and 'bannerettes' were sold; badges, belts, ties and numerous purple, white and green items were displayed and dispatched; 'Votes For Women' tea was packaged and sent to shops and by mail order to individual customers; The Woman's Press correspondence was done and visitors who dropped in with ideas were interviewed. 'General' Flora Drummond, one of the most senior organisers, had an office there.

1913

[February] Lloyd George's newly finished country house is fire-bombed. Hunger-strikes and force-feeding continue.

The suffragette bus
'A novel way of advertising the new issue was adopted . . . when an omnibus covered with notices in the purple, white and green of the Union was driven through the principal streets of the West End by Miss Douglas Smith, while Miss Barbara Ayrton [on the bottom stair] acted as conductor . . . people who cheered the women were apparently much struck by the fact that a woman should be capable of driving so ponderous a vehicle safely through the traffic. . . . A trumpeter on the roof drew attention to the omnibus as it went along, and as the various pitches were reached women alighted and left fresh supplies of the paper with the sellers'

(Left) Miss Kelly, 'a champion Votes For Women seller', was captain of the Charing Cross pitch

Much of the day-to-day running of the campaign was done by volunteers. Their contribution helped reduce the salary bill and nurtured powerful feelings of solidarity, belonging and sisterliness. By the end of 1910 the WSPU's salaried staff had grown to 110, excluding the London and regional organisers. The leadership recognised the enormous value of the volunteers' work and praised them in the WSPU's annual reports:

> It is to this splendid body of . . . workers that the extraordinary growth and development of the Union is largely due. It is they who ensure the success of every National Demonstration undertaken by the headquarters, while in the local centres they do the work of sapping and mining the strongholds of ignorance and prejudice.

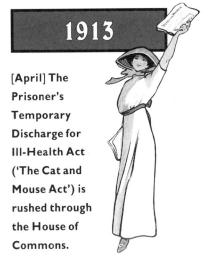

1913

[April] The Prisoner's Temporary Discharge for Ill-Health Act ('The Cat and Mouse Act') is rushed through the House of Commons.

'Do not be content with buying a single copy each week, but take in a number of copies and be responsible for selling them.'
Mary Phillips, a Scottish suffragette, selling the paper

(Right) 'General' Flora Drummond (c. 1879–1953), salaried organiser, was a 'forceful and popular speaker'
Her son, Keir Hardie Drummond, named after the leading supporter of the suffragettes in the newly emerging Labour party, was born in 1909.
By 1913 Flora Drummond had been arrested and imprisoned three times for her involvement in the campaign

1913

(Top) *In response to public disquiet about the force-feeding of hunger-striking suffragette prisoners, the government rushed through the Prisoner's Temporary Discharge for Ill-Health Act in 1913*
Known to the suffragettes as 'The Cat and Mouse Act', the prison authorities (depicted as the cat) released those on hunger-strike on a special licence and then rearrested them, like mice, returning them to prison to complete their sentences **(239)**
Designed to end the hunger-strikes and break down morale, the Act largely failed, as once the suffragette 'mice' were released they went into hiding, evaded arrest and went about committing further offences, often arson attacks in the night, for which they were rarely caught

(Bottom) *Painted cotton banner of the Chelsea WSPU* **(651)**
First unfurled at the Queen's Hall on 17 June 1908 in preparation for 'Women's Sunday' on 21 June

Hunger-striking suffragettes freed and rearrested when they recover. The Act fails because suffragette 'mice' go into hiding and commit more militant acts, for which they are rarely caught. In October force-feeding is reintroduced. The Albert Hall refuses to hire to the WSPU.

THE CAT AND MOUSE ACT
PASSED BY THE LIBERAL GOVERNMENT

BUY AND READ 'THE SUFFRAGETTE' PRICE

WOMEN'S POLITICAL SOCIAL AND UNION (CHELSEA)

VOTES FOR WOMEN

'The Game of Suffragette'
card game **(277)**

In her memoirs, Annie Kenney described the work required
of WSPU members who took an active part in the campaign:

> Nuns in a convent were not watched over and supervised
> more strictly than were the organisers and members of the
> militant movement . . . It was an unwritten rule that there
> must be no concerts, no theatres, no smoking; work and sleep
> to prepare us for more work was the . . . order of the day . . .
> I always admired the careful and methodical way in which the
> money was spent. That was why we did so much more with
> our money than the party politicians. Mere hard work would
> tell, no money was spent on advertising. If a chair would be
> suitable as a platform, why pay a few shillings for a trolley?
> If the weather was fine, why hire a hall? If the pavements were
> dry, why not chalk advertisements of the meeting instead of
> paying printers bills? If a tram would take us, why hire a taxi?
> This went on for years.

*Annie Kenney (1879–1949), salaried organiser, was 'extremely popular,
wherever she speaks she draws enormous crowds'*
*A mill girl from Oldham in Lancashire, she was one of the earliest recruits
to the WSPU, inspired by the example of the Pankhursts. She served four
prison sentences, and was the only working-class woman to attain a senior
position in the WSPU, taking over the reins of power when the leaders
were arrested in the spring of 1912 and acting as Christabel's deputy
while she was in exile in Paris. Two of her sisters and a brother also
joined the campaign*

1913

**[April] Lincoln's
Inn headquarters
raided by police:
senior staff
arrested and
papers removed.
WSPU shops and
offices all over the
United Kingdom
attacked by
indignant public.**

1913

[8 June] Emily Wilding Davison dies from injuries caused by her protest at the Derby on 4 June.

From the autumn of 1912, The Woman's Press operated from the WSPU's new headquarters at Lincoln's Inn House in Kingsway. During that year, in an angry response to the government's refusal to enable the Conciliation Bill (and hence the enfranchisement of women) to become law, the WSPU campaign became increasingly militant. Tactics such as 'Pestering the Politicians', canvassing against the Liberal Government at by-elections and general elections, and heckling cabinet ministers at public meetings gave way to new methods: window-smashing, setting fire to pillar-boxes and nationwide vandalism. In retaliation for suffragette attacks on the windows of government offices and commercial premises, in March 1912, a gang of medical students smashed The Woman's Press's windows in Charing Cross Road. The Pethick-Lawrences made clear their unhappiness with the campaign's new direction, which was led by Mrs Pankhurst and Christabel. Like others in the past who had disagreed with the Pankhurst style, they were purged from the leadership and the WSPU. The Pethick-Lawrences remained with their supporters at Clement's Inn and continued to edit and publish *Votes For Women*, and later called their branch of the WSPU the Votes For Women Fellowship. Mrs Pankhurst, Christabel, Flora Drummond and Annie Kenney ran the official WSPU from the new premises in Kingsway, and launched the official weekly, *The Suffragette*.

At 4 Clement's Inn, 1911

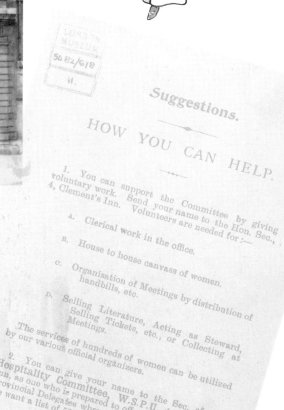

1913

Doctors who do not denounce force-feeding, or who are involved in it, are physically attacked by suffragettes.

Lincoln's Inn House, Kingsway, 1912
'Every inch of space will be fully utilised for here have to be housed all
the departments – rooms for the Honorary Secretaries and organisers,
for Editorial, Advertisement, Treasury, General Offices, Information
Department, newspaper and other filing rooms, indexing rooms, banner
departments and large secretarial staff'

'How You Can Help' handbill

Suggestions.

HOW YOU CAN HELP.

1. You can support the Committee by giving voluntary work. Send your name to the Hon. Sec., 4, Clement's Inn. Volunteers are needed for:—

   A. Clerical work in the office.

   B. House to house canvass of women.

   C. Organisation of Meetings by distribution of handbills, etc.

   D. Selling Literature, Acting as Steward, Selling Tickets, etc., or Collecting at Meetings.

   The services of hundreds of women can be utilized by our various official organizers.

2. You can give your name to the Sec. of the Hospitality Committee, W.S.P.U., 4, Clement's Inn, as one who is prepared to offer hospitality to our Provincial Delegates when they come up to London. We want a list of 500 hostesses in London.

3. You can join the Tea Table Committee. We shall be deeply grateful for your help in this purely housekeeping and domestic side of the work—of which there is a great deal to be done.

4. You can arrange Drawing invite your friends to of the Union.

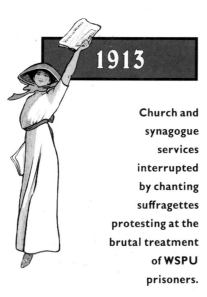

1913

Church and
synagogue
services
interrupted
by chanting
suffragettes
protesting at the
brutal treatment
of WSPU
prisoners.

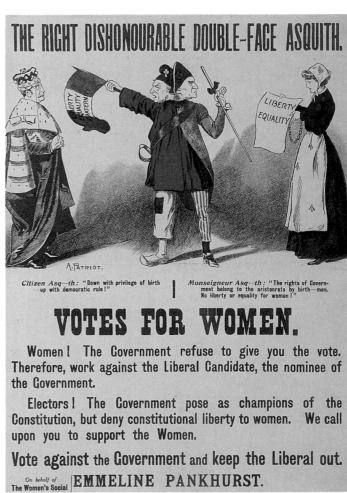

THE RIGHT DISHONOURABLE DOUBLE-FACE ASQUITH.

A. PATRIOT.

Citizen Asq—th: "Down with privilege of birth
—up with democratic rule!"

Monseigneur Asq—th: "The rights of Government belong to the aristocrats by birth—men.
No liberty or equality for women!"

VOTES FOR WOMEN.

Women! The Government refuse to give you the vote.
Therefore, work against the Liberal Candidate, the nominee of
the Government.

Electors! The Government pose as champions of the
Constitution, but deny constitutional liberty to women. We call
upon you to support the Women.

Vote against the Government and keep the Liberal out.

On behalf of
The Women's Social | EMMELINE PANKHURST.

*Alfred Pearse, who signed himself 'A Patriot', produced scores of
cartoons for the front page of* Votes For Women *and postcards and posters
like this one* **(302)**

*Prime Minister Asquith appeals to the ermine-clad crowned figure
demanding liberty, equality and fraternity, but denies liberty and equality
to the manacled suffragette prisoner*

Joan of Arc was the suffragettes' patron saint **(238)**

The Pethick-Lawrences, anxious to preserve the façade of a united movement, refused to be drawn into damaging or acrimonious discussions about their departure. *The Suffragette* explained:

Important Statement

At the first reunion of the leaders . . . Mrs Pankhurst and Christabel outlined a new militant policy which Mr and Mrs Pethick-Lawrence found themselves altogether unable to approve. Mrs Pankhurst and Christabel indicated that they were not prepared to modify their intentions and recommended that Mr and Mrs Pethick-Lawrence should resume absolute control of the paper *Votes For Women* and should leave the WSPU. Rather than make schism in the ranks of the Union, Mr and Mrs Pethick-Lawrence consented to take this course.

1913

[December]
A bomb at Holloway Gaol fails to cause much damage.

[**By the end of 1913 women in Oregon, Kansas, Arizona and Alaska given the vote.**]

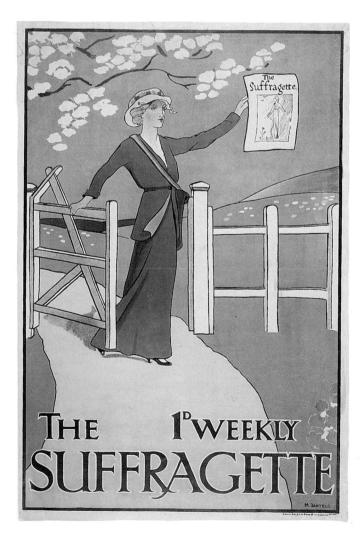

Poster advertising The Suffragette **(236)**

The last two years of the suffragettes' campaign saw an appreciable reduction in The Woman's Press's merchandising and marketing work, the key factor being the direction and atmosphere of the developing political campaign. The energy and creativity behind the three-colour goods (which appeared from the spring of 1908 onwards) were needed for more urgent political developments. For what would be the last 12 months of the suffragette campaign, The Woman's Press made a priority of producing literature and propaganda materials and some purple, white and green items, but discontinued the 'Votes For Women' tea, chocolates and cigarettes. Its eighth annual report, which covered the period March 1913 to February 1914, explained the reasons for the change in marketing policy:

> The department [The Woman's Press] has lately been reorganised. The trade in tea, chocolates, writing paper and the like has been abandoned as hardly being worthwhile in view of the very important political and educational activities of the Union, and the energies of The Woman's Press are now concentrated on the sale of their propaganda literature and of the WSPU colours.

In line with these policy changes, sales drives such as selling competitions, summer holiday campaigns and the usual poster and umbrella and parasol parades were used to maintain and increase the circulation figures of The Suffragette. The paper's distribution system was impressive; even at the height of the suffragettes' unpopularity among the public, sales were sustained. Precise circulation figures are not available – they were kept secret – but we have to assume that, although some advertisers withdrew their business, Suffragette sales were steady and rising, otherwise companies would not have continued to advertise. The Suffragette was even available abroad – in Paris at the W. H. Smith shop in the Rue de Rivoli, in Vienna at Goldschmied's and in New York at Brentano's.

Front covers of The Suffragette

1914

Sylvia Pankhurst is purged from the WSPU because her mother and her sister Christabel disapprove of the activities of her East London Federation of Suffragettes.

WSPU shops in London, 1907–14

Bow and Bromley, 298 Bow Road

Chelsea and Kensal Town, 308 King's Road, Chelsea

Chiswick, 279 High Road

Fulham and Putney, 905 Fulham Road

Hackney, 257 Dalston Lane

Hammersmith, 100 Hammersmith Road, and later 95
The Grove

Hampstead, 178 Finchley Road, later 154 Finchley Road and
89 Heath Street

Kensington, 143 Church Street (now Kensington Church
Street)

Lewisham, 107 High Street

Limehouse, 570 Commercial Road

Mile End and Bethnal Green, 34 Green Street, Bethnal Green

North West London, 215 Kilburn High Road

Paddington and Marylebone, 52 Praed Street, and later
50 Praed Street

Poplar, 174 East India Dock Road

Streatham, 55 Shrubbery Road

Sydenham and Forest Hill, 96 Kirkdale, Sydenham

Wandsworth, 47 High Street

Westminster, 17 Tothill Street

Wimbledon, 9 Victoria Crescent, The Broadway

1914

WSPU accuses the government of giving drugs to suffragette prisoners to reduce their resistance to force-feeding.

(Above) *Parasol parade advertising*
The Suffragette *newspaper in*
Erighton, April 1914

1914

[March] 'Slasher
Mary' Richardson
attacks *The
Rokeby Venus*
painting in the
National Gallery,
and is sentenced
to 18 months
in prison with
hard labour.

A suffragette demonstration in Whitehall, c. 1912
On the back of the photograph is written: 'Personally conducted or is it
a mild flirtation?' The style of placard with the arrow at the top indicates
that this suffragette may have been to prison for her involvement in the
campaign. To avoid being arrested for obstruction, she is walking in the
road and not on the pavement

China manufactured for the Women's Exhibition **(211)**
Sylvia Pankhurst's 'angel' symbol, first used in 1908, was used on a range
of items such as badges and brooches, postcard albums, banners and the
covers of the bound volumes of Votes For Women
(Loan item from the Fawcett Library, City of London Polytechnic)

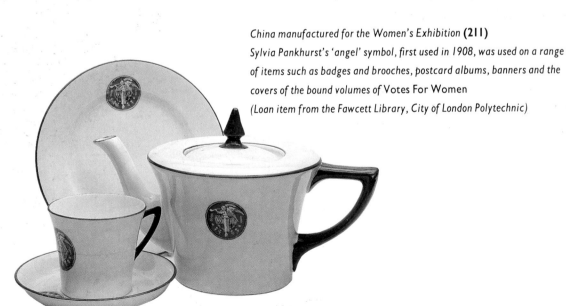

ENDPIECE

In less than eight years the WSPU's brilliantly orchestrated, thoroughly modern and highly controversial campaign had made votes for women a live political issue. The Union's shocking tactics, courage, fundraising and organisational abilities set it apart from its predecessors and contemporaries. Its language and visual imagery were peppered with militaristic and religious references. Suffragettes were comrades in livery, warriors waging a crusade for women's freedom. The commercial possibilities of the WSPU's style and political activities were exploited to the fullest extent by the Union itself, as well as suffragette entrepreneurs, political sympathisers and other commercial interests who perceived the suffragette market as lucrative. There was no area of the WSPU's operations where purple, white and green were not in evidence and used to maximum financial and propagandist advantage.

1914

[21 May]
Deputation to see King George V at Buckingham Palace fails, more than 60 women arrested. Wild scenes at Bow Street Court the following day.

(Far right) *Handbill advertising the Women's Exhibition* **(175)**
The 'Women's Exhibition and Sale of Work' was held at the Princes' Skating Rink, Knightsbridge in May 1909

A box of 'Votes For Women' soap, with Sylvia Pankhurst's design of a young woman sowing the seeds of women's suffrage **(212)**
Also used on greetings cards, handbills and badges
(Loan item from the Fawcett Library, City of London Polytechnic)

Much of the WSPU's image-building was due to the artistic and design abilities of Sylvia Pankhurst, who had trained at what is now the Royal College of Art, South Kensington. She designed the first set-piece fundraising event, the 1909 Women's Exhibition, which featured the Pethick-Lawrence colour scheme. In the two weeks it was shown it raised £6000 (£240,000 in 1992 values). The first of four logos designed by Sylvia for the WSPU – an angel standing at a signpost marked 'Freedom' and blowing a clarion call – featured prominently at this event. The WSPU changed its logo four times in almost as many years; today this would be regarded as a public relations and marketing disaster, but in fact there was no confusion about the identity. Evidence suggests that the WSPU was the first political organisation to market and merchandise its campaign, and its achievements in this field have yet to be equalled.

1914

Many historic houses, art galleries and museums, including the London Museum at Lancaster House, close to the public or admit men only in the wake of suffragette attacks on exhibits.

(Above) *Making banners for the Women's Exhibition*

The WSPU's expenditure for the year ending February 1913

The ticket desk at the Women's Exhibition
'The ladies have exercised their wonderful talents in organisation to the full and I should be surprised if any show in London will beat it in interest. The programme is a marvel of completeness'

'The most striking feature of the great exhibition will be the unity of colour . . . [it] will be carried out as far as possible through the whole of the exhibition and through the numerous stalls'

1914

Homes of suffragette sympathisers raided by the police, firms who print their newspaper threatened by the authorities. WSPU forced yet further underground, moves to new headquarters twice more.

BOADICEA

1914

[4 August] Britain at war. With the exception of Sylvia Pankhurst and her supporters who continue to fight for the vote, the suffragette campaign ends. Mrs Pankhurst and Christabel call off the militant campaign and devote themselves to encouraging men to fight in the War and to recruiting women to the munitions industry. WSPU activities cease, its name is changed to The Women's Party and *The Suffragette* newspaper is retitled *Britannia*.

So successful was the tricolour that the American women's suffrage movement, which was active in states where women were not enfranchised, was inspired to adopt colours. Alice Paul, an American who worked with the WSPU from 1909 to 1911, on her return to the United States urged her colleagues to copy some of the suffragettes' militant tactics, and they used a purple, white and gold colour scheme. It was a great compliment that WSPU tactics should be copied by American suffragists, who had a 40-year history of state-by-state enfranchisement of women.

Fundraising was vital to the success of the WSPU campaign and here it excelled. In just five years the Union's treasurer, Mrs Pethick-Lawrence, helped raise the equivalent of £3 million. The members played an important part in fundraising, involving themselves in Mrs Pethick-Lawrence's income-generating schemes, which included whist drives, exhibitions, bazaars, 'Self-Denial Weeks' and jumble sales. They also personally pledged money. It was common to place jewellery in the collecting plate which was passed around at the end of meetings. One woman donated £1000 a year (£40,000 in 1992 values), to be paid until women were given the vote. Importantly, the WSPU was backed by the support of wealthy members, most notably the Pethick-Lawrences and their peers, who provided the seed-money which was invested and used to originate many activities.

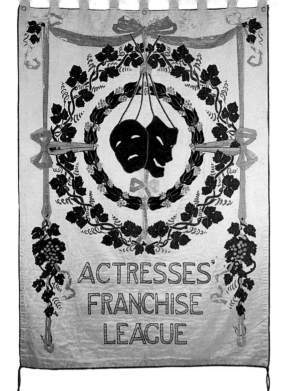

(Left) The 'Boadicea' banner made of silk, velveteen, wool, cotton and gold paint **(644)**
It was designed by Mary Lowndes (1857–1929), founder and chief organiser of the Artists' Suffrage League, in 1908

(Above) Banner of the Actresses' Franchise League, made of cotton sateen, appliquéd silk embroidery and green and gold paint **(551)**
The Actresses' Franchise League (colours pink, white and green) was founded in 1908. At least a dozen suffrage plays were published and performed by its members

1918

[February] The Representation of the People Act gives the vote to women over 30 who are householders; wives of householders; occupiers of property with an annual rent of £5 or more; or graduates of British universities.

[More than eight million women entitled to vote.]

Top row, left to right: oval silver and enamel brooch **(197)**; square silver and enamel 'Votes For Women' badge **(201)**; circular tin badge bearing a design by Sylvia Pankhurst of a young woman in (innocent) white emerging from prison walking over broken chains **(199)**
Bottom row, left to right: circular enamel WSPU badge **(195)**; shield-shaped silver and enamel pin **(196)** and shield-shaped enamel badge **(202)**

1928

All women over 21, irrespective of property qualifications, given the vote.

Sylvia Pankhurst designed this Christmas Bazaar which was held in the Portman Rooms, Baker Street in 1911
On the left stands Rose Lamartine Yates, the honorary secretary of Wimbledon WSPU, whose stall sold children's clothing

GIVEN TO BE SOLD FOR TH╎
FUNDS.

	£	s.
Gold Pendant and Chain, very old and of exquisite workmanship; pendant, heart shape, set gems, chain five rows of fine links	15	0
Ring, set single diamond	3	0
Turquoise Ring (5 stones)	3	3
Do. (7 stones)	2	10
Turquoise Signet Ring	1	1
Gold and Blue Enamel Chain Bracelet	2	0
Gold Curb Bracelet, set 5 turquoise	1	15
Gold Charm (lucky bean), set diamond	1	1
Gold Curb Bracelet	2	10
Gold Brooch	1	1
Gold and Mosaic Brooch	0	10
Two Maltese Silver Bracelets, per pair	0	15
Gold and Pearl Pin	0	12

Apply to Mrs. SANDERS, W.S.P.U., Lincoln's ╎
House. Kingsway. W.C.

(Above) The Suffragette, *January 1913*

The Suffragette, *February 1913*

56

OYEZ! OYEZ! OYEZ!

How YOU Can Help.

1. **Canvass with your collecting card.** Of all the different methods of raising money, this is the most profitable. Every member should send in a well-filled card.

2. **Send your jewels and other valuables to Headquarters,** to be sold for the good of the movement.

3. **Send goods such as farm produce,** home-made cakes, sweets, jams, marmalade, pickles, flowers and fancy articles of all kinds to be sold at our London and Provincial W.S.P.U. Shops — not forgetting Lincoln's Inn House.

4. **Arrange any of the following either in your own home or in halls:** Teas, Soirees, Whist Drives, Cake and Candy Sales, Jumble Sales, Theatricals, Dances, Concerts, White Elephant Sales, Housewife Sales, Bazaars, "Shilling Parcel" Teas, Home-made Sales, American Teas, Advertisement Teas, &c.

5. **The following open-air schemes are in hand,** help with some of them:— Street selling of flowers, home-made sweets and fruit. Violin playing in the street. Pavement artists. Stalls in country markets. Barrows of fruit and flowers to be taken round in town and country. Street collecting.

Do you want to know how to organise any of the above schemes? Then write to the Self-Denial Secretary, Mrs. Dacre Fox, at Lincoln's Inn House, or, better still, come and see her. She will tell you all you want to know.

Even as late as 1950, 30 years after the introduction of the vote in Britain, some suffragettes continued to proclaim their allegiance. Mary Leigh, the Drum Major of the WSPU's Drum and Fife Band, attended George Bernard Shaw's funeral service and unfurled a purple, white and green flag, shouting that he had been one of the suffragettes' best friends during their fight for the vote. She was removed by the police.

To conclude, a reminder of the suffragettes' own perception of the importance of their colours:

> Last summer [1908] with a swiftness that surprised us all, the colours of the WSPU became universally known. . . Today the very children can tell you that the suffragette colours are purple, white and green and at the sight of them cry 'Votes For Women'. To members of the Union, the tricolour is full of meaning and they now understand the full devotion of a regiment to its colours.

1969

Representation of the People Act reduces the age of voting from 21 to 18.

'Self-Denial Weeks' were held every year to raise funds for the 'war chest'
These are Bristol suffragettes in 1910

THE WOMAN

THE CLOCK THAT HAS **NOT** BEEN PUT BACK.

A. PATRIOT

1869.
Wyoming.

1893.
Wyoming.
New Zealand.
Colorado.

1896.
Wyoming.
New Zealand.
Colorado.
S. Australia (1894).
Utah.
Idaho.

1902.
Wyoming.
New Zealand.
Colorado.
S. Australia.
Utah.
Idaho.
W. Australia (1900).
New South Wales.

1907.
Wyoming.
New Zealand.
Colorado.
S. Australia.
Utah.
Idaho.
W. Australia.
New South Wales.
Tasmania (1904).
Queensland (1905).
Finland.

19
Wyoming.
New Zeal
Colorado.
S. Austral
Utah.
Idaho.
N. S. Wal
W. Austra
Tasmania.
Queensland
Finland.
Victoria.
Norway.

SEE HOW SHE

O T E R

LIST OF
EXHIBITS

1911.	**1912-13.**	
Wyoming.	Wyoming.	Tasmania.
New Zealand.	New Zealand.	W. Australia.
Colorado.	Colorado.	N. S. Wales.
S. Australia.	S. Australia.	Oregon.
Utah.	Utah.	Kansas.
Idaho.	Idaho.	Arizona.
W. Australia.	Queensland.	Alaska.
New South Wales.	Finland.	
Tasmania.	Victoria.	
Queensland.	Norway.	
Finland.	Washington.	
Victoria.	California.	
Norway.		
Washington (1910).		
California.		

GROWS !

An illustration from Votes For
Women, *June 1913*
*Women's suffrage had been granted
in many other places long before
Great Britain (1918 and 1928)*

Women's suffrage in other countries

1. Photograph	Alice Paul, *c.* 1910; 155mm × 100mm
2. Photograph	Miss Flatman and Mrs Martel, *c.* 1911; 140mm × 90mm
3. Handbill	'What Woman Suffrage Means in New Zealand', Lady Stout, NWSPU, *c.* 1909; 260mm × 190mm
4. Pamphlet	*The Women's Vote in Australia*, Mrs Martel, The Woman's Press, 1906; 220mm × 140mm
5. Pamphlet	*The Cape Parliament and the Enfranchisement of Women*, Irene M. Ashby Macfadyen, African Book Company, *c.* 1907; 250mm × 160mm
6. Pamphlet	*Woman Suffrage in America: A Reply to Mrs Humphrey Ward*, Mrs Philip Snowden, Wadsworth and Co., 1909; 220mm × 140mm
7. Pamphlet	*Australia's Advice: The Debate in the Australian Senate on the Votes for Women Resolution*, 17 November 1910, abridged from the official report, The Woman's Press, 1911; 185mm × 125mm
8. Pamphlet	*Woman Suffrage in Finland*, Madame Aino Malmberg, Women's Freedom League, *c.* 1909; 220mm × 140mm
9. Pamphlet	*Women's Suffrage in Many Lands*, Alice Zimmern, 1909; 165mm × 100mm
10. Pamphlet	*Where Women Have the Vote*, National Union of Women's Suffrage Societies, 1909; 220mm × 140mm
11. Newspaper	*Votes For Women*, bound volume vi, WSPU, 13 June 1913; 650mm × 430mm × 40mm

---

All printed items are in sepia or black and white unless stated otherwise.
WSPU = Women's Social and Political Union
NWSPU = National Women's Social and Political Union

| 12. Poster | 'Convicts and Lunatics Have no Vote in Parliament – Should All Women be Classed with These?', Emily J. Harding Andrews, 1908; 980mm × 740mm *By permission of the Fawcett Library, City of London Polytechnic* |

Why did women want the vote?

| 13. Postcard | in Esperanto, requesting information on courses in Esperanto given by suffragettes, c. 1910; 90mm × 140mm Translation: |

      Friendly Greetings!

      Hey, let's ring out a new song

      For the language Esperanto,

      By writers and by poets

      In poems and in odes.

| 14. Postcard | 'No Vote – No Tax', c. 1909; 90mm × 140mm John Bull: 'Of course you must pay your share of his wages, but remember, my dear, this is my servant and he is not engaged to take your instructions.' Mrs Bull: 'In that case I can't afford to pay your servant, John; I must keep my money to pay those who will carry out my instructions.' |

| 15. Postcard | 'Anti-Suffragisms Illustrated', Alfred Pearse ('A Patriot'), 1910; 90mm × 140mm 'A Woman's Place is in the Home, Who Will then Earn the Daily Bread?' |

| 16. Postcard | 'How the Law Protects the Daughters', 'MaC', 1909; 90mm × 140mm English girls (crying): 'Nurse says we had better get used to the baby brother taking our things, because when we grow up we sha'nt have anything, he will take it all.' French girls: 'What a shame; the brothers and sisters have equal shares in our country.' |

| 17. Postcard | 'How the Law Protects the Husband', c. 1909; 90mm × 140mm Husband's marriage vow: 'With all my Worldly Goods I thee endow.' Which means by the law of England, that a man need only keep his wife from becoming a charge on the Ratepayers, be he rich or poor. |

18. Postcard   'The Scylla and Charybdis of the Working Woman', M. Hughes, c. 1912;
                    90mm × 130mm

19. Postcard   'How the Law Protects the Widower', 'MaC', c. 1909; 90mm × 140mm
                    Widower: 'My wife has left no will.'
                    Law: 'Then all her property is yours; had you died, she would only have
                    got a third of your property.'

20. Postcard   'How the Law Protects the Widow', c. 1909; 90mm × 140mm
                    Widow: 'Can nothing alter my husband's will?'
                    Law: 'No, Madam, a man may leave his money to whom he likes, but you
                    must maintain your children, that is one of the laws of England.'

21. Postcard   'Is this Right?', 'M.L.' (possibly Mary Lowndes), c. 1910; 90mm × 140mm
                    Woman: 'Why can't I have an umbrella too?'
                    Voter: 'You can't. You ought to stop at home.'
                    Woman: 'Stop at home indeed! I have my Living to earn.'

22. Postcard   'Dear Young Ladies', K.F. Powell, c. 1910; 90mm × 140mm
                    'You are left PENNILESS, your father's estates are entailed and everything
                    goes to a distant cousin, BECAUSE YOU ARE WOMEN.'

23. Postcard   'Votes For Women', hand-coloured, c. 1910; 90mm × 140mm
                    A poor, bare-footed woman weighed down by a heavy burden

24. Postcard   'Who Spends the Taxes?', H.S. Adkins, c. 1910; 90mm × 140mm
                    'Look here, I am going to spend my penny – I shall buy just what I like
                    with them 'cause I'm a man, and you'll have to stay outside and take what
                    I get you, 'cause you're only a woman.'

25. Postcard   'Waiting for a Living Wage', Catherine Courtauld, c. 1913; 90mm × 140mm
                    Starvation haunted the lives of female sweated workers – here a chain-
                    maker

26. Pamphlet   *Why Women Desire the Franchise*, Frances Power Cobbe, London National
                    Society for Women's Suffrage, 1869; 190mm × 110mm

27. Pamphlet   *A Brief Review of the Women's Suffrage Movement Since Its Beginning in 1832
                    to 1910*, 1911; 180mm × 120mm

28. Pamphlet	*The Women's Charter of Rights and Liberties*, Lady McLaren, preliminary draft, private circulation, 1909; 220mm × 140mm

29. Pamphlet	*Pebbles from the Brook – Being Three Meditations Upon the Anti-Suffrage State of Mind*, R.F. Cholmeley, reprinted from *The Englishwoman*, 1913; 220mm × 140mm

30. Pamphlet	*An Outsider's View of the Woman's Movement*, Florence Bright, WSPU, 1906; 220mm × 150mm

31. Pamphlet	*Under His Roof*, Elizabeth Robins, Women Writer's Suffrage League, c. 1912; 215mm × 140mm

32. Pamphlet	*Mary Wollstonecraft and the Women's Movement of To-Day*, Margaret S. Clayton, Frank Palmer, c. 1907; 220mm × 140mm

33. Postcard	photograph of suffragettes selling *The Great Scourge* and *The Suffragette* newspaper, c. 1914; 90mm × 140mm

34. Pamphlet	*How Women Use the Vote*, A. Maude Royden, National Union of Women's Suffrage Societies, 1912; 185mm × 25mm

35. Pamphlet	*Woman Under the Law*, W.G. Earengey, Women's Freedom League, 1908; 145mm × 105mm

36. Pamphlet	*For and Against*, Lady Sybil Smith, The Woman's Press, c. 1910; 220mm × 140mm

37. Pamphlet	*Women and Citizenship: A Summary of the Present Position*, Women's Co-operative Guild, 1904; 185mm × 120mm

38. Pamphlet	*The Women's Suffrage Movement: I. Why Should We Care for It?, II. How Can We Help to Further It?*, Emily Davies, Central Society for Women's Suffrage, 1905; 220mm × 140mm

39. Pamphlet	*The ABC of Votes For Women*, Marion Holmes, Women's Freedom League, c. 1910; 210mm × 140mm

40. Pamphlet	*Votes and Wages: How Women's Suffrage Will Improve the Economic Position of Women*, A. Maude Royden, National Union of Women's Suffrage Societies, 1911; 220mm × 140mm

41. Pamphlet   *The Case for Woman's Suffrage and Objections Answered*, Thomas Johnston, Forward Printing and Publishing Company, *c.* 1908; 220mm × 140mm

42. Pamphlet   *Working Women and the Poor Law*, B.L. Hutchins, Women's Industrial Council, 1909; 220mm × 140mm

43. Pamphlet   *The Militant Methods of the N.W.S.P.U.*, Christabel Pankhurst, The Woman's Press, 2nd ed., 1908; 220mm × 140mm

44. Pamphlet   *The Importance of the Vote*, Mrs Pankhurst, The Woman's Press, 11th ed., 1914; 220mm × 140mm

45. Handbill   'Why We Oppose the Liberal Government', The Woman's Press, *c.* 1906; 300mm × 210mm

46. Handbill   'Do Not Give Women the Vote!', Revd Marie Jennay, The Woman's Press, *c.* 1910; 300mm × 210mm
An imaginary anti-suffrage speech

47. Handbill   'Why Women Want the Vote', The Woman's Press, *c.* 1906; 300mm × 210mm

48. Handbill   'Is the English Law Unjust to Women?', F.W. Pethick-Lawrence, The Woman's Press, *c.* 1910; 300mm × 210mm

49. Handbill   'The Urgency of Woman Suffrage', The Woman's Press, *c.* 1907; 300mm × 210mm

50. Handbill   'The Labour of Married Women: A Working Woman's Reply to Mr John Burns', Jennie Baines, The Woman's Press, *c.* 1908; 300mm × 210mm

51. Handbill   'What Women Get, And What They Need', Christabel Pankhurst, *c.* 1905; 300mm × 210mm

52. Handbill   'How the Press Deceives the Public', The Woman's Press, 1907; 300mm × 210mm

53. Handbill   'The Militant Methods', Christabel Pankhurst, The Woman's Press, *c.* 1908; 300mm × 210mm

54. Handbill	'The Tactics of the Suffragettes', Emmeline Pethick-Lawrence, The Woman's Press, *c.* 1907; 300mm × 210mm
55. Handbill	'A Challenge!', Christabel Pankhurst, WSPU, 1912; 300mm × 210mm
56. Handbill	advertising a demonstration in Hammersmith, WSPU, *c.* 1906; 220mm × 180mm
57. Handbill	'A Message from the WSPU', The Woman's Press, *c.* 1910; 300mm × 210mm
58. Handbill	'Woman This, and Woman That', The Woman's Press, *c.* 1910; 300mm × 210mm
59. Programme	for a suffragette reception at Essex Hall, Essex Street, Strand, *c.* 1907; 200 × 100mm
60. Book	*An Anti-Suffrage Alphabet Book*, ed. Laurence Housman, privately published, 1911; 380mm × 260mm
61. Pamphlet	six suffragette songs, NWSPU, *c.* 1908; 220mm × 140mm

Songs and plays

62. Music for four songs	tied in purple, white and green ribbon, Wimbledon WSPU, *c.* 1909; 200mm × 210mm
63. Songsheet	'The March of the Women', Ethel Smyth, three-colour design by Margaret Morris, signed by Mrs Pankhurst on 28 August 1911, The Woman's Press, 1911; 310mm × 230mm
64. Play	*Lady Geraldine's Speech: A Comedietta*, Beatrice Harraden, Women Writer's Suffrage League, 1911; 155mm × 125mm
65. Play	*A Chat with Mrs Chicky: A Duologue*, Evelyn Glover, Actresses' Franchise League, 1912; 130mm × 100mm

66. Play	*An Allegory*, Vera Wentworth, Actresses' Franchise League, *c.* 1909; 124mm × 100mm
67. Play	*A Woman's Influence*, Gertrude Jennings, Actresses' Franchise League, *c.* 1909; 125mm × 100mm
68. Play	*The Mother's Meeting*, Mrs Harlow Phibbs, Actresses' Franchise League, *c.* 1909; 125mm × 100mm
69. Play	*An Anti-Suffragist, or The Other Side*, H.M. Paull, Actresses' Franchise League, *c.* 1909; 125mm × 100mm
70. Play	*Mary Edwards*, P.R. Bennett, Actresses' Franchise League, 1911; 125mm × 100mm
71. Play	*The Apple*, Inez Bensusan, Actresses' Franchise League, *c.* 1909; 125mm × 100mm
72. Play	*Mrs Appleyard's Awakening*, Evelyn Glover, Actresses' Franchise League, *c.* 1910; 125mm × 100mm
73. Play	*Lady Butterby and Mrs MacBean*, 'S.', *c.* 1912; 180mm × 120mm
74. Songsheet	'The March of the Women', Ethel Smyth, The Woman's Press, 1911; 190mm × 120mm
75. Play	*How the Vote Was Won*, Cicely Hamilton and Christopher St John, Garden City Press, 1909; 185mm × 120mm
76. Play	*Alice in Ganderland*, Laurence Housman, The Woman's Press, 1911; 190mm × 120mm
77. Songsheet	'The Women of England', W. Ward-Higgs, *c.* 1910; 200mm × 130mm
78. Songsheet	'Bermondsey Voters Keep the Liberal Out!', NWSPU, *c.* 1908; 190mm × 130mm
79. Songsheet	'To Mrs Pankhurst and her Fellow Prisoners in Holloway Gaol', 1908; 190mm × 110mm
80. Songsheet	'Keep the Liberal Out!', 'J.G.', Herbert Sinclair et al, *c.* 1908; 190mm × 130mm

The 'Antis'

81. Pamphlet   *The Women's National Anti-Suffrage League*, 1909; 220mm × 140mm

82. Handbill   'Votes For Women. NEVER!', advertising a meeting in Trafalgar Square
             on 16 July 1910, Anti-Suffrage Campaign, 1910; 220mm × 140mm

83. Pamphlet   *Sir Almroth Wright's Case against Woman Suffrage answered by Bernard*
             Shaw, Irishwomen's Suffrage Federation, c. 1913; 185mm × 125mm

84. Book   *The Unexpurgated Case against Woman Suffrage*, Sir Almroth E. Wright,
             Constable and Co., 1913; 230mm × 150mm

85. Pamphlet   *Votes for Catherine, Sarah and Melligan*, Kathleen Ainslie, Castell Brothers
             Ltd, 1910; 150mm × 130mm

86. Pamphlet   *Women's Suffrage: Some Sociological Reasons for Opposing the Movement*,
             Mrs E.M. Simon, Cornish Brothers Ltd, 1907; 220mm × 140mm

87. Pamphlet   *Woman, or Suffragette? A Question of National Choice*, Marie Corelli, 1907;
             185mm × 130mm

88. Postcard   cartoon, 'Home, Sweet Home', 'Tom B.', colour, 1909; 90mm × 140mm
             A scene of domestic violence, with handwritten annotation: 'Striking
             Example of a Suffragette's Home – If They *Have* Any Homes'
             Sent to 'Miss Pankhurst and Her Crew'. The message on the reverse reads:
             'You set of sickening fools – if you have no homes, no husbands – no
             children – no relations – why don't you drown yourselves out of the way?'

89. Postcard   cartoon, colour, c. 1909; 90mm × 140mm
             'Great Suffrage Demonstration, Miss Hissy [Christabel Pankhurst as a
             goose] addresses a meeting of the Goose's Social and Political Union:
             Every proper goose should have her own propagander!'

90. Postcard   cartoon, (?) Thomas Penny, c. 1910; 90mm × 140mm
             Suffragettes attacking policemen: 'Women can't fight, can't they!!'

91. Postcard   photograph, 'The Suffragette at Home and at Work', c. 1909;
             90mm × 140mm
             A baby girl at home, holding a newspaper in her hand, and at work,
             standing on a chair addressing an imaginary crowd

92. Postcard

cartoon, 'The Suffragette Nails her Colours to the Mast', 'N.P.', colour, c. 1910; 90mm × 140mm

A masculine-looking woman ties a 'Votes For Women' flag to her umbrella

93. Postcard

cartoon, 'The Harem Scarem – the Trousers at Last', 'Reg P.', c. 1909; 90mm × 140mm

A suffragette in men's clothing

94. Postcard

cartoon, 'How the Deuce did I Know She was a Suffragette?', Donald McGill, colour, c. 1913; 90mm × 140mm

A man forcibly ejected from a house

95. Postcard

cartoon, Arthur Moreland, colour, 1906; 90mm × 140mm

Two fierce, masculine-looking suffragettes talk to a working-class woman on her doorstep:

'But surely, my good woman, don't you yearn for something beyond sufficient money to provide you with your immediate needs, doesn't your heart swell with the thought of elevating your sex to share in making the laws of your country?'

Reply: 'I ain't got no time, mum.'

96. Postcard

cartoon, 'The Suffragette Defies the Tyrant Man', 'N.P.', colour, c. 1910; 90mm × 140mm

A tiny, masculine-looking suffragette harangues a very large policeman

97. Postcard

cartoon, 'What *are* Men, *Who* are They, *Where* are They?', Arthur Moreland, colour, 1906; 90mm × 140mm

A large, mannish-looking woman addressing a meeting of women

98. Postcard

cartoon, 'I Protest Against Man-made Laws', Arthur Moreland, colour, 1906; 90mm × 140mm

Angry, unattractive suffragettes on trial

99. Postcard

mock-Christmas greetings to suffragette hunger-strikers, with hunger-strike medal collaged on, c. 1913; 95mm × 140mm

100. Postcard

cartoon, 'The Suffragette Flouts His Worship', colour, c. 1910; 90mm × 140mm

A judge peers down at two suffragettes demanding 'Votes For Women'. The use of exaggerated scale reinforces the insignificance of their campaign

101. Postcard

cartoon, 'The Suffragettes' Vision – Mrs Speaker', colour, c. 1910;
90mm × 140mm

Two severe-looking women in charge of the House of Commons

102. Postcard

cartoon, 'This Session! Just a Line to Mr Asquith!', colour, c. 1911;
90mm × 140mm

A little girl posts a letter to the Prime Minister. The cartoon is ridiculing the
suffragettes' attempts to persuade the government to grant women the vote

103. Postcard

photograph, 'Who Said Rats?', c. 1909; 90mm × 140mm

A female toddler, dressed up as a blue-stocking suffragette, reading
a newspaper

104. Postcard

cartoon, 'Fifi the Militant', George Piper, colour, c. 1912; 90mm × 140mm

Fifi, a clockwork cat, wearing a 'Votes For Women' sash and holding a
hammer in her paw, addresses other toys from the toy cupboard

105. Postcard

colour cartoon, Wall, c. 1914; 90mm × 140mm

A petulant and precocious little girl says: 'Votes For Women – and you
think you can keep women silent politically? IT CAN'T BE DID!'

106. Postcard

photograph, 'Fellow Women, Our Day Dawns at Last', c. 1909;
90mm × 140mm

The same female toddler as **103**

107. Postcard

photograph, 'An Advokate for Women's Rights', colour, c. 1912;
90mm × 140mm

A cat dressed in a hat and a purple, white and green shawl fastened with
a 'Votes For Women' badge

108. Postcard

photograph, c. 1912; **90mm** × 140mm

A cat wearing a straw **boater** demands 'Votes For Women'

109. Postcard

cartoon, colour, c. 1913; 90mm × 140mm

A grinning black cat: '**Your luck's in!** Where's that vote you promised
me?'

110. Postcard

cartoon, 'A Prominent Suffragette of the Stone Age', Frederic G. Dutton,
1909; 90mm × 140mm

A suffragette wearing an animal skin has carved 'Votes For Women' in
a block of stone

111. Postcard

cartoon, 'This is "The House" that Man Built', colour, c. 1908;
90mm × 140mm

   And these are a few of the women of note

   Who say that they want, and they will have the vote?

   And they think that they ought? To have Man's *support*:

   Even though HE should have to go short? The sly Suffragette

   who is all on the get

   And wants all, in the House that man built.

112. Postcard

cartoon, 'We Want the Vote', colour, 1909; 90mm × 140mm
A grotesquely ugly woman. The message on the reverse reads: 'Dear
Christie, Don't you think you had better sew a button on my shirt? Yours,
Joe.'
Sent to Christabel Pankhurst at Clement's Inn

113. Postcard

cartoon, colour, 1908; 90mm × 140mm
Three men panic at the arrival of three determined-looking suffragettes.
Handwritten annotation: 'God help mere man'

114. Bell

green ceramic, labelled 'The Suffragette' on the front, the handle
represents the head of an old crone, on the back is the name 'Barion',
c. 1909; height 150mm

Lampooning the 'Antis'

115. Postcard

cartoon, 'On the Cromer Beach', E. Hartley-Wilson, c. 1910;
90mm × 140mm
A mother and her children on the sands at Cromer, an allusion to
Lord Cromer, one of the most vocal opponents of women's suffrage.
The incoming tide of 'Votes For Women' is about to engulf the Anti-
Suffrage League's sandcastle:
Alarmed mother: 'Children!! The tide is coming in! You will be swept
away!'
Children (reassuringly): 'Oh no, Mummy, don't you see the sandcastle
we have made to STOP IT.'

116. Postcard | cartoon, 'Ye Anti-Suffrage League', Charles Lane Vicary, colour, 1908; 90mm × 140mm

Half a dozen aristocratic ladies wearing crowns drive a motor car bearing the sign, 'We have *all* we want! No Votes For Women'

117. Postcard | cartoon, 'King Asquith Canute and the Inevitable Tide', Isabel Pocock, 1909; 90mm × 140mm

Prime Minister Asquith, dressed as Canute, foolishly tries to hold back the tide of woman's suffrage

118. Postcard | cartoon, 'The New Mrs Partington', Ernestine Mills, colour, c. 1910; 90mm × 140mm

Mrs Partington, a leading light of the 'Antis', hopelessly tries to sweep back the advancing tide of the demand by Liberal women, medical women, taxpayers, etc, for the vote: 'Somehow the tide keeps rising!'

119. Postcard | cartoon, 'J.H.D.' (thought to be Joan Harvey Drew), c. 1910; 90mm × 140mm

Two members of the Anti-Suffrage League wearing old-fashioned clothes made of *The Times* and *Spectator* meet John Bull.
John Bull: 'Very charming, I'm sure; but aren't you a little behind the times?'

120. Postcard | cartoon, 'G.R.P.', c. 1910; 90mm × 140mm

Miss Bull offers her father a steaming cup of 'Votes For Women':
'Come along, Daddy, drink it up. You don't know how much good it may do those rheumatic pains of yours.'

121. Postcard | cartoon, 'C.H.' (possibly Clemence Housman) and 'D.M.', c. 1910; 90mm × 140mm

Boys and girls from Finland, New Zealand, Australia and Norway are eating franchise cake. Jane Bull asks: 'Give me a bit of your Franchise Cake, Johnnie.' He tells her it would not be good for her. She replies: 'How can you tell if you won't let me try it? It doesn't hurt those other little girls.'
Women in Finland had been given the vote in 1906, in New Zealand in 1893, in Australia between 1893–1909 and those in Norway in 1907

122. Postcard | cartoon, 'The Anti-Suffrage Ostrich', Catherine Courtauld, c. 1909; 90mm × 140mm

Despite the fact that the sun ('Women's Freedom') is rising, the ostrich has its head in the sand ('Ignorance' and 'Stupidity') and insists: 'The sun is NOT rising.'

123. Postcard

cartoon, 'The Anti-Suffrage Society as Portrait Painter', Catherine Courtauld, *c.* 1912; 90mm × 140mm

The Anti-Suffrage Society has painted the calm and sedate Britannia as a screaming harridan, 'Britannia Unsexed', wielding the vote in her clenched fist. The artist, with the head of an ass (the Society's initials) warns: 'This, my dear Mrs Britannia, is a true and authentic portrait of yourself if ever you get the vote.'

124. Postcard

cartoon, 'The Anti-Suffrage Society as Prophet', Catherine Courtauld, *c.* 1912; 90mm × 140mm

The prophet, with the head of an ass (the Society's initials), exclaims: 'Woe and desolation! Behold a woman-enfranchised England prostrate beneath her descending foes!' (a reference to attack by Germany)

125. Postcard

cartoon, 'The Anti-Suffragist Butterfly', Ernestine Mills, poem by C.P. Stetson, colour, *c.* 1910; 90mm × 140mm

'I do not want to fly', said she,

'I only want to squirm!'

She drooped her wings dejectedly

But still her voice was firm.

'I do not want to be a fly,

I want to be a worm!'

O yesterday of unknown lack!

Today of unknown bliss!

I left my fool in red and black,

The last I saw was this:

The creature madly climbing back

Into her chrysalis!

126. Postcard

cartoon, 'Anti-Suffragist Types', L. Thompson-Price, *c.* 1909; 90mm × 140mm

'The man who thinks that "Women have no right to vote because they can't defend their country"' (dedicated to the Anti-Suffrage Society)

127. Postcard

cartoon, 'Types of Anti-Suffragists', L. Thompson-Price, *c.* 1909; 90mm × 140mm

A glum, unattractive man: 'The Parliamentary Candidate who thinks "that the women would be sure to vote for the handsomest man!"' (dedicated to the Anti-Suffrage Society)

128. Postcard	cartoon, 'The Anti-Suffrage Society as Dressmaker', Catherine Courtauld, *c.* 1912; 90mm × 140mm The dressmaker, with the head of an ass (the Society's initials) assures her client that the old-fashioned and ill-fitting gown she has made is right for her: 'Out of date, and a bad fit? *Impossible*, Madam! I assure you it must *suit* you, for I have it exactly after your grandmother's pattern.'
129. Postcard	cartoon, 'This is "The House" that Man Built', *c.* 1910; 90mm × 140mm A woman Speaker presides over male and female members of parliament: But oh what a wonderful change inside The women as well as the men preside They both hold the reins & no one complains, For the men now admit that the ladies have brains And are every bit as fitted to sit As themselves, in this House that man built.
130. Postcard	cartoon, 'The Growing Movement', *c.* 1909; 90mm × 140mm The strength of the opposition to women's suffrage is ridiculed by the scale of the images – a very large bird ('Woman Suffrage') perches on a tiny bush ('Opposition'): There was an old man who said 'Hush! I perceive a young bird in this bush.' When they said, is it small? he replied – 'Not at all! It is four times as big as the bush!'
131. Postcard	cartoon, 'This is Our First Task', Frederic G. Dutton, 1909; 90mm × 140mm Two suffragettes, spades in hand, stand ready to uproot the tree of 'deep-rooted prejudices'
132. Postcard	cartoon, 'The Prehistoric Argument', Catherine Courtauld, 1912; 90mm × 140mm A Stone Age couple stand at the door of their cave, No. 1, Cavern Villas. Primeval woman: 'Why can't I go out too and see the world?' Primeval man: 'Because you can't. Woman's proper sphere is the Cave.'
133. Handbill	advertising a meeting of the imaginary 'Antediluvian Society' at Stonehenge, poking fun at the 'Antis', WSPU, *c.* 1909; 300mm × 210mm
134. Pamphlet	*Beware! A Warning to Suffragists*, rhymes by Cicely Hamilton, sketches by M. Lowndes, D. Meeson-Coates, C. Hedley-Charlton, Artists' Suffrage League, *c.* 1908; 170mm × 235mm

The London headquarters

135. Photograph   WSPU headquarters (from autumn 1912), Lincoln's Inn House, Kingsway, 1912; 170mm × 160mm

136. Postcard   photograph of the general offices, Lincoln's Inn House, Kingsway, 1912; 90mm × 140mm

137. Postcard   photograph of the editorial department, Clement's Inn, Strand, 1911; 90mm × 140mm

138. Postcard   photograph of the general offices, Clement's Inn, Strand, 1911; 90mm × 140mm

139. Postcard   photograph of the advertising department, Clement's Inn, Strand, 1911; 90mm × 140mm

140. Postcard   photograph of the dispatch department, Clement's Inn, Strand, 1911; 90mm × 140mm

141. Postcard   photograph of the information bureau, Clement's Inn, Strand, 1911; 90mm × 140mm

142. Postcard   photograph of the entrance hall, Lincoln's Inn House, Kingsway, 1912; 90mm × 140mm

143. Postcard   photograph of the treasury department, Clement's Inn, Strand, 1911; 90mm × 140mm

144. Postcard   photograph of the ticket office, Clement's Inn, Strand, 1911; 90mm × 140mm

145. Postcard   photograph of Miss Jessie Kenney's office, Clement's Inn, Strand, 1911; 90mm × 140mm

146. Postcard   photograph of the duplicating office, Clement's Inn, Strand, 1911; 90mm × 140mm

147. Postcard   photograph of the *Votes For Women* newspaper being packed at The Woman's Press, 156 Charing Cross Road, 1911; 90mm × 140mm

148. Postcard	photograph of the typists' office, Clement's Inn, Strand, 1911; 90mm × 140mm
149. Postcard	photograph of Mrs Pethick-Lawrence's office, Clement's Inn, Strand, 1911; 90mm × 140mm

Selling the newspaper

150. Postcard	photograph of 'press carts' delivering *Votes For Women* to various pitches in central London, July 1911; 90mm × 140mm
151. Postcard	photograph of Miss Kelly, a champion *Votes For Women* seller, July 1911; 90mm × 140mm
152. Postcard	photograph of three young suffragettes holding placards advertising *Votes For Women*, c. 1911; 90mm × 140mm
153. Postcard	photograph of a 'parasol parade' in Brighton selling *The Suffragette*, April 1914, the signatures of the women on the reverse; 90mm × 140mm
154. Postcard	studio portrait of Miss Grace Chappelon wearing a poster advertising *Votes For Women*, October 1911; 90mm × 140mm
155. Photograph	Miss Barbara Ayrton on the bottom stair of the *Votes For Women* bus, October 1909 (the date on the photograph is incorrect); 215mm × 165mm
156. Photograph	suffragettes on a 'poster parade' selling *Votes For Women*, (*second left*) Miss Mabel Capper, (*fourth left*) Miss Mary Gawthorpe, June 1908; 120mm × 165mm
157. Photograph	Miss Mary Phillips selling *Votes For Women*, October 1907; 200mm × 220mm
158. Photograph	a group of women taking part in a 'poster parade' to promote *The Suffragette*, July 1914; 210mm × 155mm
159. Photograph	two suffragettes selling *The Suffragette* at Henley Regatta, July 1913; 110mm × 150mm

| 160. Photograph | a suffragette selling *Votes For Women*, April 1909; 170mm × 120mm |
| 161. Photograph | a 'press cart' delivering *Votes For Women*, February 1909; 150mm × 210mm |

The Christmas Bazaar, 1911

162. Postcard	photograph of Wimbledon WSPU's stall at the Christmas Bazaar, Portman Rooms, Baker Street, 1911; 90mm × 130mm
163. Postcard	photograph of the Christmas Bazaar, Portman Rooms, Baker Street, 1911; 90mm × 130mm
164. Programme	for 'the Christmas Fair and Festival, 1911', purple, white and green cover, The Woman's Press, 1911; 250mm × 150mm

Style and imagery

165. Postcard	photograph of Miss Elsie Howey on horseback dressed as Joan of Arc, April 1909; 90mm × 130mm
166. Photograph	Miss Charlotte Marsh holding a WSPU flag, December 1908; 200mm × 100mm
167. Photograph	Miss Annan Bryce on horseback dressed as Joan of Arc, leading the Women's Coronation Procession, 17 June 1911; 210mm × 170mm
168. Newspaper	*The Suffragette*, loose copy, WSPU, 13 March 1914; 270mm × 190mm

The Women's Exhibition, May 1909

169. Postcard	photograph of the catalogue and enquiries stall at the 'Women's Exhibition and Sale of Work in the Colours', Princes' Skating Rink, Knightsbridge, May 1909; 90mm × 140mm
170. Postcard	photograph of part of Sylvia Pankhurst's mural for the Women's Exhibition, 1909; 90mm × 140mm
171. Postcard	photograph of a procession advertising the Women's Exhibition, May 1909; 90mm × 140mm
172. Postcard	photograph of the crowded Women's Exhibition, May 1909; 90mm × 140mm
173. Postcard	photograph of 'General' Flora Drummond standing at a stall at the Women's Exhibition, May 1909; 90mm × 140mm
174. Postcard	photograph of the joint stall of Brighton, Hove, Putney and Fulham WSPU branches, the Women's Exhibition, May 1909; 90mm × 140mm
175. Handbill	advertising the Women's Exhibition, purple, white and green, NWSPU, May 1909; 230mm × 140mm
176. Catalogue	listing the Women's Exhibition 'Political Peepshows (Political cartoon in model)', NWSPU, May 1909; 200mm × 135mm
177. Handbill	advertising the Women's Exhibition, purple, white and green, NWSPU, May 1909; 260mm × 190mm
178. Photograph	the Women's Band (led by Mrs Mary Leigh) advertising the Women's Exhibition, May 1909; 105mm × 165mm
179. Photograph	women making banners for the Women's Exhibition, May 1909; 170mm × 220mm
180. Photograph	a ticket stall at the Women's Exhibition, May 1909; 160mm × 210mm

The Woman's Press and WSPU shops

181. Postcard   photograph of The Woman's Press, 156 Charing Cross Road, May 1910; 90mm × 140mm

182. Postcard   photograph of purple, white and green merchandise in the front window of The Woman's Press, 156 Charing Road, May 1910; 90mm × 140mm

183. Postcard   photograph of the interior of The Woman's Press, 156 Charing Cross Road, September 1911; 90mm × 140mm

184. Postcard   photograph of Laura Ainsworth, c. 1909; 90mm × 140mm
Laura Ainsworth organised 'poster parades' from 156 Charing Cross Road

185. Postcard   photograph of the interior of The Woman's Press, 156 Charing Cross Road, 1910; 90mm × 140mm
A wide range of purple, white and green and 'Votes For Women' merchandise is visible

186. Postcard   photograph of a 'press cart' outside The Woman's Press, 156 Charing Cross Road, July 1911; 90mm × 140mm

187. Postcard   photograph of the North West London WSPU shop, 215 Kilburn High Road, c. 1910; 90mm × 140mm

188. Postcard   photograph of a WSPU shop and office, location unknown, c. 1913; 90mm × 140mm

189. Postcard   photograph of the Fulham and Putney WSPU shop, 905 Fulham Road, c. 1910; 90mm × 140mm

190. Postcard   photograph, thought to be of the Hampstead WSPU shop, 178 Finchley Road, 1912; 90mm × 140mm

191. Postcard   photograph of the Scarborough WSPU shop, 39 Huntriss Road, c. 1913; 90mm × 140mm

192. Postcard   photograph of the Reading WSPU shop, 39 West Street, 1910; 90mm × 140mm

193. Postcard	photograph, thought to be of the Wimbledon WSPU shop, 9 Victoria Crescent, The Broadway, c. 1911; 90mm × 140mm

The Woman's Press: merchandising

194. Button badge	tin, portrait of Mrs Pankhurst, sepia, c. 1909; diameter 20mm
195. Badge	circular, enamel, with the initials 'WSPU', purple, white and green, c. 1908; diameter 35mm
196. Pin	shield-shaped, enamel and silver, with the words 'Votes For Women', purple, white and green, c. 1909; 25mm × 25mm, overall length 40mm
197. Brooch	oval-shaped, silver and enamel, in purple, white and green, c. 1910; 30mm × 130mm
198. Belt buckle	plated brass, embossed with the 'Haunted House' design (see **310**), 1908; 60mm × 70mm The buckle would have been worn with a purple, white and green ribbon-belt
199. Badge	tin, with Sylvia Pankhurst's design of a woman in white emerging from captivity stepping over heavy chains and carrying 'Votes For Women' streamers, purple, white and green, 1908; diameter 30mm
200. Hatpin	silver, in the shape of a prison convict's arrow, c. 1909; length 60mm, width of arrowhead 20mm
201. Badge	square, enamel and silver, with the words 'Votes For Women', purple, white and green, c. 1908; 25mm × 25mm
202. Badge	shield-shaped, enamel, with the words 'Votes For Women – WSPU', purple, white and green, c. 1908; 20mm × 20mm
203. Necklace	glass beads, purple, white and green, c. 1909; length 560mm

204. Necklace   paste, purple, white and green, *c.* 1909; length 250mm, width of design 120mm
Believed to have been worn by Mrs Pankhurst

205. Buttons   silk satin with silk embroidery, purple, white and green, *c.* 1909; diameter 20mm
By permission of the Fawcett Library, City of London Polytechnic

206. Rosette ribbon   silk, purple, white and green, *c.* 1908; length 290mm, diameter of rosette 70mm

207. Rosette ribbon   silk, purple, white and green, *c.* 1908; length 630mm, diameter of rosette 80mm

208. Rosette badge and ribbons   silk, the badge has the initials 'E.P.' (Emmeline Pankhurst), purple, white and green, *c.* 1908; diameter of rosette 45mm, length of ribbons 60mm

209. Badge   silver and glass, with medallion portrait of Mrs Pankhurst and purple, white and green silk ribbons, *c.* 1908; diameter of portrait 40mm

210. Rosette badge and ribbons   silk, the badge has the words 'Votes For Women', purple, white and green, *c.* 1908; diameter of rosette 55mm, length of ribbons 100mm

211. Teaset   china, with Sylvia Pankhurst's 'angel' design, purple, white and green, manufactured by Williamsons, Longton, Staffordshire, 1909
The 13 pieces are a teapot and four teacups, saucers and teaplates; height of teapot with lid 150mm, diameter of teaplate 175mm, diameter of saucer 130mm, diameter of teacup 75mm
By permission of the Fawcett Library, City of London Polytechnic

212. Box of soap   containing four bars of 'Votes For Women' buttermilk soap, the lid bears Sylvia Pankhurst's design of a woman scattering the seeds of women's suffrage, purple, white and green, 1912; box 145mm × 145mm, bar of soap 70mm × 45mm
By permission of the Fawcett Library, City of London Polytechnic

213. Tie   silk, knitted, purple, white and green, 1910; 810mm × 33mm
By permission of the Fawcett Library, City of London Polytechnic

214. Calendar   for 1912, with Sylvia Pankhurst's design of a woman scattering the seeds of women's suffrage, purple, white and green; 130mm × 70mm, fully opened 290mm × 130mm
By permission of the Fawcett Library, City of London Polytechnic

215. Photograph	(*left to right*) Miss Mary Leigh, Mrs Jennie Baines, Miss Mabel Capper, c. 1908; 200mm × 250mm
216. Postcard	purple, white and green, 1912; 90mm × 140mm Sylvia Pankhurst's 'angel' design, with watercolour thistles and the slogan 'We fight for our rights. WSPU'
217. Book	*The Suffrage Annual and Women's Who's Who*, ed. 'A.J.R.', Stanley Paul & Co., 1913; 190mm × 150mm × 50mm
218. Postcard	'To Greet You', purple, white and green, c. 1912; 90mm × 130mm Sylvia Pankhurst's design of a woman scattering the seeds of women's suffrage, with a quotation by James Russell Lowell: What men call luck Is the prerogative of valiant souls, The fealty life pays its rightful kings.
219. Postcard	'With Best Xmas Wishes', purple, white and green, c. 1912; 125mm × 90mm Sylvia Pankhurst's design of a woman scattering the seeds of women's suffrage, with a verse from 'Neale's "Egypt"'
220. Greetings card	'To Wish You Well in 1914', purple, white and green; 90mm × 140mm A young suffragette holding a 'Votes For Women' flag looks to the horizon where the sun ('Freedom') rises: 'Hail life and death and all that bring the goal in sight'
221. Postcard	purple, white and green, 1910; 90mm × 140mm 'Rebellion to tyrants is obedience to God. Purple – Freedom White – Purity Green – Hope'
222. Postcard	'A Merry Christmas and Votes for Women in 1910', purple, white and green, 1910; 90mm × 140mm A drummer-girl dressed in the purple, white and green uniform of the Women's Band
223. Greetings card	in the style of an embroidered sampler, purple, white and green, c. 1912; 100mm × 140mm

224. Postcard	'With Best Wishes for Xmas and the New Year 1908–9', purple, white and green; 90mm × 140mm Sylvia Pankhurst's design of a woman in white emerging from captivity and stepping over her chains
225. Postcard	'Votes For Women' motif in purple, white and green in top lefthand corner, *c.* 1909; 90mm × 150mm
226. Postcard	'Women's Emancipation – Justice, Truth, Equity and Comradeship', Mary Slee, purple, white and green, *c.* 1913; 90mm × 140mm
227. Postcard album	purple, white and green, *c.* 1909; 360mm × 240mm × 60mm Sylvia Pankhurst's design of a woman in white emerging from captivity and stepping over her chains
228. Postcard album	purple, white and green, *c.* 1909; 280mm × 240mm × 30mm Sylvia Pankhurst's design of a woman in white emerging from captivity and stepping over her chains
229. Postcard	chorus of 'The Purple, White and Green March', R.H. Potts, 1910; 90mm × 140mm

Hark to the fife! Hark to the drum! WSPU
Who will obey the call and come? WSPU
Purple a-flutter with white and green, WSPU
What do the tricolour standards mean? WSPU

Purple stands for the loyal heart,
Loyal to cause and King;
White for purity, **Green** for hope,
Bright hopes of spring,

March and fight through the long, long night
That our children be brave and free!
March and fight for our one common right,
Citizens to be!

230. Handkerchief	linen, white with purple and green border, *c.* 1908; 360mm × 350mm
231. Handkerchief	cotton, white, with the figure of a suffragette holding a 'Votes For Women' flag embroidered in coloured silks in one corner, *c.* 1909; 420mm × 420mm
232. Scarf	silk, striped in purple, white and green, 'Votes For Women' printed at either end, 1908; 212mm × 33mm

233. Postcard	photograph of Laura Ainsworth wearing her Holloway brooch and hunger-strike medal, *c.* 1910; 90mm × 140mm
234. Greetings card	purple, white and green tied with purple ribbon, 1912; 155mm × 110mm Joan of Arc in full armour
235. Christmas card	designed by Hilda Dallas, purple, white and green, 1911; 145mm × 105mm Father Christmas gives 'Votes For Women'
236. Poster	advertising *The Suffragette*, Mary Bartels, colour, *c.* 1912; 750mm × 500mm
237. Poster	'Let Them Starve. Views of Public Men', *The Standard*, 9 June (?1912); 770mm × 520mm
238. Poster	advertising *The Suffragette*, Hilda Dallas, purple, white and green, November 1911; 750mm × 520mm A suffragette dressed as Joan of Arc in full armour, wearing a tabard saying 'Justice' and holding a WSPU flag
239. Poster	advertising *The Suffragette*, with 'The Cat and Mouse' design, purple, white and green, *c.* 1914; 750mm × 50mm
240. Poster	'Ruthless War on Militants: Crushing Action', *The Globe*, *c.* 1914; 750mm × 520mm
241. Poster	'Chasing Suffragettes – Police and the Mob', *Daily Chronicle*, 28 April (?1910); 750mm × 550mm

Dramatis Personae

242. Bust	Mrs Pankhurst, bronze, from a model worked in Holloway Gaol by Miss Alice Morgan Wright, 1912; 180mm × 100mm
243. Ostrich feather	purple, worn by Mrs Pankhurst at the 'Rush the House of Commons' deputation, 13 October 1908; length 310mm
244. Shoe	leather, glass beads and silk bow, black, belonging to Mrs Pankhurst, *c.* 1912; 245mm × 65mm

245. Collar	wool, cream, embroidered in purple and green silk by Mrs Pankhurst, *c.* 1911; 130mm × 500mm
246. Postcard	photograph of Mrs Pankhurst, *c.* 1909; 90mm × 140mm
247. Postcard	photograph of Miss Christabel Pankhurst, *c.* 1909; 90mm × 140mm
248. Postcard	photograph of Miss Sylvia Pankhurst, *c.* 1910; 90mm × 140mm
249. Postcard	photograph of Mr Frederick Pethick-Lawrence, *c.* 1909; 210mm × 140mm
250. Postcard	photograph of Mrs Emmeline Pethick-Lawrence, *c.* 1909; 90mm × 140mm
251. Postcard	photograph of 'General' Flora Drummond, June 1908; 90mm × 140mm
252. Postcard	photograph of Miss Emily Wilding Davison, *c.* 1910; 90mm × 140mm
253. Postcard	photograph of Mrs Mabel Tuke, *c.* 1911; 90mm × 140mm
254. Postcard	photograph of Mrs Charlotte Despard, *c.* 1908; 90mm × 140mm
255. Postcard	photograph of Mrs Edith How-Martyn, *c.* 1908; 90mm × 140mm
256. Postcard	photograph of Mrs Theresa Billington Greig, *c.* 1908; 90mm × 140mm
257. Postcard	photograph of Mrs Mary Leigh, the Drum-Major of the Women's Band, *c.* 1909; 90mm × 140mm
258. Postcard	photograph of Mrs Minnie Baldock, *c.* 1908; 90mm × 140mm
259. Postcard	photograph of Miss Vera Holme, WSPU chauffeuse, *c.* 1909; 90mm × 140mm
260. Postcard	photograph of Miss Elsie Howey, *c.* 1909; 90mm × 140mm
261. Postcard	photograph of Miss Annie Kenney, 1908; 210mm × 150mm
262. Postcard	photograph of Miss Adela Pankhurst, *c.* 1908; 90mm × 140mm
263. Postcard	photograph of Miss Jessie Kenney, *c.* 1909; 90mm × 140mm

264. Postcard	photograph of Miss Mary Gawthorpe, c. 1908; 90mm × 140mm
265. Postcard	photograph of Mrs Nellie Alma Martel, c. 1908; 90mm × 140mm
266. Postcard	photograph of Miss Ada Flatman (far right), with a group of suffragettes in replica prison clothing, c. 1912; 85mm × 135mm
267. Postcard	photograph of Mrs Mansell Moullin (a leading Welsh suffragette), 1911; 90mm × 140mm
268. Postcard	photograph of Miss Vera Wentworth, c. 1908; 90mm × 140mm
269. Postcard	photograph of Miss Grace Roe, 1914; 90mm × 140mm
270. Photograph	a suffragette procession (far right Lady Constance Lytton), summer 1910; 220mm × 170mm
271. Photograph	Miss Christabel Pankhurst being modelled at Madame Tussaud's, 1908; 150mm × 200mm
272. Photograph	Miss Sylvia Pankhurst addressing a small crowd at the headquarters of her East End suffragettes in Bow Road, 1912; 120mm × 150mm
273. Postcard	photograph of some of the leading lights of the WSPU, c. 1908; 90mm × 140mm (Bottom row, left to right, from third left) Miss Mary Gawthorpe, Miss Christabel Pankhurst, Mrs Emmeline Pethick-Lawrence, Miss Annie Kenney (Top row, far left) Miss Dorothy Pethick, sister of Mrs Pethick-Lawrence, (far right) Miss Jessie Kenney
274. Postcard	photograph of Mrs Pankhurst at a railway station during a tour of the country, c. 1911; 90mm × 140mm
275. Postcard	photograph of Mrs Rose Lamartine Yates and her son Paul, c. 1911; 90mm × 140mm

Merchandising and fundraising

276. Card game — 'Panko or Votes for Women', pictures by E.T. Reed of *Punch*, purple, white and green, 1909; 50 cards, each 105mm × 75mm

277. Card game — 'The Game of Suffragette', *c.* 1908; 52 cards, each 100mm × 80mm

278. Optical toy — 'Elusive Christabel', two parts, colour, 1912; 140mm × 90mm

279. Tablecloth — linen, white, embroidered with white linen thread, lacis insertions depict policemen, suffragettes holding 'Votes For Women' placards and classical designs, knitted cotton border, *c.* 1910; 1250mm × 1250mm

280. Game — 'Suffragettes In and Out of Prison: Find the Way Out of Gaol', with tiny wooden dice, *c.* 1908; board 250mm × 170mm

281. Pencil — purple with 'Votes For Women' in white, *c.* 1909; 170mm × 5mm

282. Game — 'Pank-a-Squith', board only, no pieces, colour, *c.* 1909; 560mm × 480mm

283. Handkerchief — paper, souvenir programme of the procession from the Embankment to the Albert Hall, colour, 18 June 1910; 390mm × 390mm

284. Handkerchief — paper, souvenir of the procession from the Embankment to the Albert Hall, colour, 18 June 1910; 390mm × 390mm

285. Notepaper — single sheet of Chelsea WSPU stationery, *c.* 1910; 210mm × 270mm

286. Playing cards — pack of standard cards, with 'Votes For Women' and the prison arrow design in purple, white and green, *c.* 1908; 65mm × 25mm × 95mm, each card 60mm × 90mm

Office window of The Woman's Press shop

287. Handbill — 'A Campaign Fund', WSPU, 1906; 250mm × 190mm

288. Pamphlet — *Report of Self-Denial Week*, The Woman's Press, 1908; 240mm × 160mm

289. Postcard	photograph of suffragettes taking part in a 'Self-Denial Week', Bristol, 1910; 90mm × 140mm
290. Handbill	'Fund for £20,000', WSPU, c. 1908; 250mm × 400mm
291. Collecting card	for a 'Self-Denial Week', 1914, purple, white and green; 250mm × 130mm
292. Report	*First Annual Report*, for the year ending 28 February 1907, WSPU; 240mm × 160mm
293. Report	*Second Annual Report*, for the year ending 29 February 1908, and accounts for The Woman's Press, 1 January–31 December 1907, The Woman's Press; 240mm × 160mm
294. Report	*Third Annual Report*, for the year ending 28 February 1909, and accounts for The Woman's Press, 1 January–31 December 1908, with Sylvia Pankhurst's 'angel' design in purple, white and green on the front cover, The Woman's Press; 240mm × 160mm
295. Report	*Fourth Annual Report*, for the year ending 28 February 1910, and accounts for The Woman's Press, 1 January–31 December 1909, with Sylvia Pankhurst's design of a woman scattering the seeds of women's suffrage on the front cover, purple, white and green, The Woman's Press; 240mm × 160mm
296. Report	*Fifth Annual Report*, for the year ending 28 February 1911, and accounts for The Woman's Press, 1 January–31 December 1910, with the same design as **295** on the front cover, purple, white and green, The Woman's Press; 240mm × 160mm
297. Report	*Sixth Annual Report*, for the year ending 29 February 1912, and accounts for The Woman's Press, 1 January–31 December 1911, with the same design as **295** on the front cover, purple, white and green, The Woman's Press; 240mm × 160mm
298. Report	*Seventh Annual Report*, for the year ending 28 February 1913, with Joan of Arc in full armour on horseback on the front cover, purple, white and green, The Woman's Press; 240mm × 160mm
299. Report	*Eighth Annual Report*, for the year ending 28 February 1914, with Joan of Arc (standing) in full armour holding a flag on the front cover, purple, white and green, The Woman's Press; 240mm × 160mm

300. Banner	'The Office', velvet, silk twill, silk, braid and paint, rectangular, with a design of three black crows with quills in their beaks, designed by Mary Lowndes, black, yellow and orange, 1908; 1240mm × 880mm
301. Banner	'Marie Curie', silk, cotton, velvet and metal braid, yellow, zigzag bottom edge, with 'Marie Curie' above 12 radiating panels in velvet appliqué and 'Radium' outlined in braid, designed by Mary Lowndes, 1908; 1300mm × 920mm

The Woman's Press

302. Poster	cartoon, 'The Right Dishonourable Double-Face Asquith', Alfred Pearse ('A Patriot'), purple, white and green, 1910; 480mm × 330mm Prime Minister Asquith appeals to the ermine-clad crowned figure, demanding liberty, equality and fraternity, but denies liberty and equality to the manacled suffragette prisoner: 'Women! The Government refuse to give you the vote. Therefore work against the Liberal Candidate, the nominee of the Government. Electors! The Government pose as champions of the Constitution, but deny constitutional liberty to women. Vote against the Government and keep the Liberal out.'
303. Poster	'The Vain Search for Christabel', *Evening News*, 1912; 760mm × 520mm
304. Poster	'Wild Scene in The Commons', *Daily Express*, 15 July (?1909); 750mm × 550mm
305. Poster	cartoon, 'The Anti-Suffrage Ostrich', Catherine Courtauld, colour, c. 1909; 1150mm × 760mm Despite the fact that the sun ('Women's Freedom') is rising, the ostrich has its head in the sand ('Ignorance' and 'Stupidity') and insists: 'The sun is NOT rising.'
306. Poster	'Polling Station', colour, c. 1912; 750mm × 930mm The male gentry, agricultural labourers and factory-workers had been enfranchised during the 19th century, whereas worthy women such as mothers, academics, civic dignitaries and myriad others had not been granted equal citizenship with men

307. Poster	'The Appeal of Womanhood', Louise Jacobs, 1912; 950mm × 650mm A woman stands in front of a group of cowed, miserable women (some in chains), holding a scroll with the demand: 'We want the vote to stop the white slave traffic, sweated labour and to save the children.'
308. Poster	'Waiting for a Living Wage', colour, Catherine Courtauld, c. 1913; 750mm × 500mm Starvation haunted the lives of female sweated workers, here a chainmaker
309. Poster	'London Magistrate Marches with Suffragettes', *Evening News*, c. 1911; 720mm × 520mm
310. Poster	'The Haunted House', David Wilson, *Daily Chronicle*, 1907; 1000mm × 800mm The ghostly figure of a suffragette hovers above the House of Commons, holding a piece of paper saying 'Votes For Women' in her hand
311. Poster	'There Was an Old Dame in a Huff', colour, 1912; 900mm × 700mm An elderly woman scowls at a group of women carrying a banner with the slogan 'Woman Suffrage': There was an old dame in a huff; Women don't want the vote she cried: – 'Stuff!' When they said – 'But we do,' she answered 'Pooh, pooh! I don't – and let that be enough!'

'Women's Sunday', 21 June 1908

312. Sash	silk ribbon, purple, white and green with 'Votes For Women' woven in purple on white, 1908; 100mm × 565mm, unfolded 1130mm
313. Sash	silk moiré, green with 'Group Captain' in silver paint, silver metallic tassel, 1908; 100mm × 590mm, unfolded 1180mm
314. Sash	silk moiré, purple with 'Banner Captain' in silver paint, silver metallic tassel, 1908; 105mm × 570mm, unfolded 1100mm *By permission of the Fawcett Library, City of London Polytechnic*

315. Sash	silk ribbon, purple, white and green with 'Colour Distributor' printed in black, 1908; 60mm × 300mm, unfolded 600mm *By permission of the Fawcett Library, City of London Polytechnic*
316. Peaked cap	wool, purple, white and green with gold-coloured metal braid and the initials 'NWSPU' embroidered in silk, leather peak Presented by Toye and Co., makers of medals and regalia, to 'General' Flora Drummond, 1908; crown diameter 270mm, inner diameter 180mm
317. Sash	silk velvet, gold-coloured, decorated with 'General' and 'Votes For Women' embroidered in green and purple silk, gold-coloured metallic braid and tassels Presented by Toye and Co., makers of medals and regalia, to 'General' Flora Drummond, 1908; 105mm × 500mm, unfolded 1000mm
318. Epaulette	silk velvet, cream and gold-coloured, decorated with gold-coloured metal braid and tassels Presented by Toye and Co., makers of medals and insignia, to 'General' Flora Drummond, 1908; 45mm (narrowest point) × 110mm (widest point) × 140mm, length of tassels 80mm
319. Badge	silk, white, with 'Speaker' embroidered in purple silk, 1910; 120mm × 55mm
320. Badge	silk, white, with 'Banner Captain' and 'NWSPU' embroidered in purple silk, gold-coloured metallic tassel, 1908; 170mm × 50mm
321. Badge	silk, white, with 'Chairman' and 'NWSPU' embroidered in purple silk, 'NWSPU' encircled by a gold-coloured metal laurel wreath, 1908; 210mm × 50mm
322. Ribbon	silk, purple, white and green, c. 1908; 900mm × 45mm
323. Postcard	photograph of four suffragettes in a boat on the River Thames advertising 'Women's Sunday', June 1908; 90mm × 140mm
324. Postcard	photograph of 'Mrs Drummond opposite the Terrace of the House of Commons addressing M.P.s, inviting them to the Hyde Park demonstration', June 1908; 90mm × 140mm
325. Postcard	photograph of 'Hyde Park Demonstration, Sunday, June 21, 1908; Miss Christabel Pankhurst LLB and Mrs Pethick Lawrence'; 90mm × 130mm

326. Postcard	photograph of platform 6 in Hyde Park, 'Women's Sunday', 21 June 1908; 90mm × 140mm
327. Postcard	photograph of Miss Elsa Gye (wearing a Banner Captain sash), Miss Douglas Smith (holding a convict's arrow) and Miss Aeta Lamb, c. 1908; 90mm × 140mm
328. Three tickets	for 'Women's Sunday', purple, white and green, 21 June 1908; 30mm × 60mm
329. Photograph	'General' Flora Drummond (rear view, in regalia), Mrs Pethick-Lawrence and Miss Christabel Pankhurst in academic robes on 'Women's Sunday', 21 June 1908; 170mm × 120mm
330. Photograph	ten suffragettes wearing 'Votes For Women' sashes and hats held in place with 'Votes For Women' silk scarves, in a boat on the River Thames advertising 'Women's Sunday', June 1908; 200mm × 170mm
331. Photograph	crowds in Hyde Park on 'Women's Sunday', June 1908; 160mm × 100mm
332. Photograph	banners being prepared for 'Women's Sunday', June 1908; 160mm × 215mm
333. Photograph	one of the processions to Hyde Park led by Mrs Pankhurst (left), Miss Christabel Pankhurst (centre) and Miss Annie Kenney (right), 21 June 1908; 130mm × 215mm
334. Photograph	suffragettes carrying banners to Hyde Park, 21 June 1908; 140mm × 210mm
335. Photograph	Mrs Pethick-Lawrence (left) and Mr Israel Zangwill (right) standing in front of a banner declaring 'Women's Will Beats Asquith's Won't' en route to Hyde Park, 21 June 1908; 140mm × 200mm
336. Photograph	platform 5, Hyde Park, 21 June 1908; 95mm × 155mm
337. Photograph	a procession walking past the Houses of Parliament en route to Hyde Park, 21 June 1908; 190mm × 230mm
338. Photograph	a procession and several banners passing the Houses of Parliament en route to Hyde Park, 21 June 1908; 190mm × 260mm
339. Photograph	preparing banners for 'Women's Sunday', June 1908; 200mm × 150mm

340. Photograph   a procession and several banners en route to Hyde Park, 21 June 1908; 155mm × 190mm

341. Photograph   crowds passing the Houses of Parliament en route to Hyde Park, 21 June 1908; 160mm × 220mm

342. Postcard   photograph of 'Great Votes For Women Demonstration in Hyde Park, Sunday, June 21, 1908', showing a large crowd and numerous banners from WSPU branches all over the country; 90mm × 140mm

343. Letter   two sheets, describing 'Women's Sunday', dated 21 June 1908; 250mm × 200mm, 230mm × 175mm

344. Letter   to the police requesting access to Hyde Park on 21 June 1908, signed by ('General') Mrs Flora Drummond, dated 21 June 1908; 255mm × 210mm

345. Newspaper   *Votes For Women*, bound volume i, WSPU, 25 June 1908; 220mm × 330mm, opened out 470mm × 330mm

346. Photograph   suffragettes carrying a banner titled 'Deeds Not Words, Office Staff, NWSPU', en route to 'Women's Sunday', 21 June 1908; 220mm × 200mm

347. Handbill   urging Hammersmith women to take part in 'Women's Sunday', June 1908; 195mm × 120mm

'Deeds Not Words'

348. Photograph   a policeman removing a suffragette poster from railings, 19 March 1909; 120mm × 160mm

349. Photograph   a procession of suffragettes released from Holloway Gaol walking down Kingsway; in the lead, Mrs Mary Leigh (*left, carrying placard*), Miss Annie Kenney (*centre*) and Mrs Minnie Baldock (*right*), c. 1909; 150mm × 200mm

350. Photograph   WSPU members, wearing replica prison clothing and carrying a banner saying 'Welcome', greet suffragettes released from Holloway Gaol, 1908; 170mm × 210mm

351. Photograph	a meeting in Trafalgar Square to celebrate the release of Mrs Pankhurst, Miss Christabel Pankhurst and 'General' Flora Drummond, December 1908; 130mm × 190mm
352. Photograph	'Human Letters to Downing Street', two suffragettes outside No. 10 attempt to speak to Prime Minister Asquith, 23 January 1909; 110mm × 160mm
353. Photograph	'Human Letters to Downing Street', two suffragettes outside No. 10 (see **352**) joined by a small crowd of curious men and boys, 23 January 1909; 170mm × 100mm
354. Photograph	suffragettes advertising the deputation to the House of Commons (30 June 1908), June 1908; 270mm × 170mm
355. Photograph	suffragettes wearing replica prison clothing campaign at the Chelmsford by-election from the top of an omnibus, December 1908; 110mm × 160mm
356. Photograph	Mrs Olive Fergus (*left*) attempting to speak to Prime Minister Asquith and Mrs Frank Corbet in Downing Street, 1908; 190mm × 270mm
357. Photograph	two suffragettes (*left* Emma Sproson) chalking the pavement, c. 1908; 90mm × 140mm
358. Photograph	Miss Gladice Keevil campaigning at the Manchester by-election 1907; 160mm × 120mm
359. Photograph	suffragettes wearing replica prison clothing advertising a prisoner's procession at Holloway Gaol, 7 November 1908; 100mm × 150mm
360. Photograph	three suffragettes equipped to chain themselves to railings (*right* Vera Holme), 1909; 160mm × 120mm
361. Shackle and chain	iron, c. 1908; width of handcuff 80mm wide, length of chain 280mm
362. Harness, shackle and chain	leather and iron, used by suffragettes to chain themselves to the railings of public buildings, c. 1908; harness 120mm × 800mm, diameter 280mm, length of chain 600mm
363. Photograph	suffragettes wearing replica prison clothing advertising a 'protest meeting' outside Holloway Gaol, 7 November 1908; 150mm × 200mm

364. Photograph   a procession of suffragettes wearing replica prison clothing cheer
Mrs Pankhurst as they march past Holloway Gaol, 7 November 1908;
110mm × 155mm

365. Photograph   a meeting in Trafalgar Square of suffragettes wearing replica prison
clothing to welcome Mrs Jennie Baines on her release from Holloway Gaol,
12 December 1908; 165mm × 120mm

366. Resolution   'carried at a meeting of women, held in the Caxton Hall, Westminster,
on Thursday, February 13 1908', signed by Mrs Pankhurst, 1908;
250mm × 210mm
'This meeting of women is of the opinion that the most urgent of all
constitutional reforms is to make the House of Commons representative
of the people by enfranchising the women of the country. This meeting
therefore calls upon the Government, before dealing with the position of
the House of Lords, to secure that the will of the people shall prevail in
the House of Commons by granting the vote to duly qualified women.'

367. Photograph   released suffragette prisoners wearing replica prison clothing in an
open-top vehicle, October 1908; 160mm × 100mm

368. Photograph   released suffragette prisoners wearing replica prison clothing, c. 1909;
130mm × 90mm

369. Photograph   suffragettes prisoners wearing replica prison clothing en route to cheer
Mrs Pankhurst in Holloway Gaol, 7 November 1908; 120mm × 160mm

370. Postcard   photograph of suffragettes wearing replica prison clothing and holding
WSPU flags, campaigning against the Liberals at the Chelmsford by-
election, December 1908; 90mm × 140mm
(*Back row, left*) Miss Ada Flatman, Miss C. Auld
(*Front row*) Miss Joachim, Miss Elsa Gye, 'General' Flora Drummond,
Miss Keegan, Miss Kelly

371. Postcard   photograph of suffragette prisoners in replica prison clothing campaigning
at the Chelmsford by-election, accompanied by a male brass band,
December 1908; 90mm × 140mm

372. Photograph   suffragettes campaigning at St Pancras during the General Election,
January 1910; 220mm × 120mm

373. Promise card	to refuse to take part in the 1911 Census, WSPU, 1911; 220mm × 140mm
374. Pamphlet	*The Census: News From No-Man's Land*, Laurence Housman, Women's Freedom League, 1911; 120mm × 95mm

Emily Wilding Davison

375. Postcard	photograph of 'The Late Miss Emily Wilding Davison' in academic robes, *c.* 1909; 90mm × 140mm
376. Photograph	Miss Emily Wilding Davison in academic robes, *c.* 1909; 150mm × 80mm
377. Framed picture	containing Miss Emily Wilding Davison's leather purse, her return ticket to Victoria Station and an insurance ticket, found on her body, 4 June 1913; 270mm × 225mm *By permission of the Fawcett Library, City of London Polytechnic*
378. Framed madonna lily	carried at Miss Emily Wilding Davison's funeral, 14 June 1913; 500mm × 400mm × 40mm *By permission of the Fawcett Library, City of London Polytechnic*
379. Framed group	*The Suffragette Derby*, showing P.C. Burn's account of Miss Emily Wilding Davison's protest at the Derby, 4 June 1913, a photograph of the incident and transcription, June 1913; 830mm × 570mm *By permission of the Metropolitan Police Museum*
380. Postcard	with Christmas greetings by Miss Emily Wilding Davison, 1912; 90mm × 140mm
381. Photograph	Miss Emily Wilding Davison's funeral procession in Hart Street, London, Saturday, 14 June 1913; 110mm × 150mm
382. Photograph	the hearse arriving at St George's Church, Bloomsbury, 14 June 1913; 160mm × 110mm
383. Postcard	photograph of suffragettes guarding Miss Emily Wilding Davison's coffin at Victoria Station, 14 June 1913; 90mm × 140mm

384. Pamphlet *In Memoriam Miss Emily Wilding Davison*, for the memorial service, 14 June 1914; 190mm × 130mm

385. Order of Memorial Service for Miss Emily Wilding Davison, 6 June 1914, purple on white; 210mm × 130mm

386. Pamphlet *The Life of Emily Wilding Davison: An Outline*, G. Colmore, The Woman's Press, 1913; 185mm × 110mm

387. Fragment satin, triangular-shaped, purple, white and green, reputedly from a sash worn by Miss Emily Wilding Davison when she made her protest at the Derby, 1913; 45mm × 60mm
Accompanied by card label, International Women's Franchise Club Ltd

388. Postcard photograph of Miss Emily Wilding Davison's coffin leaving St George's Church, Bloomsbury, 14 June 1913; 90mm × 140mm

389. Photograph suffragettes carrying one of seven purple silk banners bearing the words 'Fight On and God Will Give the Victory' ahead of the hearse, 14 June 1913; 110mm × 150mm

390. Photograph the funeral procession leaving Morpeth railway station, Sunday, 15 June 1913; 240mm × 300mm

391. Postcard photograph of the funeral procession in Morpeth, 15 June 1913; 90mm × 140mm

392. Photograph a large crowd watching the funeral procession make its way to the cemetery, Morpeth, 15 June 1913; 240mm × 300mm

393. Newspaper *Votes For Women*, loose copy, WSPU, 13 June 1913; 270mm × 385mm

'Deeds Not Words': campaigning

394. Photograph Miss Una Dugdale standing on a chair to address a small crowd of men, October 1908; 100mm × 150mm

395. Photograph	three suffragettes with a banner belonging to Lewisham, Deptford and Greenwich WSPU holding an outdoor meeting, c. 1910; 110mm × 85mm
396. Postcard	photograph of ten suffragettes, including Mrs Pankhurst (centre right) and 'General' Flora Drummond (far left) campaigning against the Liberals, c. 1910; 90mm × 140mm
397. Postcard	photograph of 'poster parade' of members of Ealing WSPU advertising a meeting on Ealing Common, 1 June 1909; 90mm × 140mm
398. Postcard	photograph of suffragettes outside a WSPU shop, 1909; 90mm × 140mm
399. Postcard	photograph of a suffragette addressing a crowd of men from a tradesman's cart, c. 1910; 90mm × 140mm
400. Postcard	photograph of suffragettes campaigning against the Liberals at the Cleveland by-election, July 1909; 90mm × 140mm
401. Postcard	photograph of suffragettes campaigning against the Liberal Government, (second left) Mrs Martel, (centre) Mrs Pankhurst, (far right) Adela Pankhurst, c. 1910; 90mm × 140mm
402. Postcard	photograph of six suffragettes standing in front of WSPU committee rooms during a by-election campaign, c. 1910; 90mm × 140mm
403. Book	*The Women's Suffrage Cookery Book*, compiled by Mrs Aubrey Dowson, Women's Printing Society Ltd, 1910; 210mm × 170mm *Private collection*
404. Photograph	'General' Flora Drummond canvassing, October 1907; 170mm × 220mm
405. Photograph	a suffragette holding a placard saying 'Give Women the Vote This Session' decorated with a convict's arrow (suggesting she may have been to prison for the cause) talks to a policeman, c. 1912; 170mm × 190mm The message on the reverse reads: 'Whitehall – Personally conducted or is it a mild flirtation?'
406. Photograph	Miss Emma Sproson distributing handbills from a tradesman's cart, 5 May 1908; 210mm × 160mm
407. Photograph	suffragettes campaigning at the Stepney by-election, (seated left) 'General' Flora Drummond, (second left) Mrs Minnie Baldock, 1907; 115mm × 150mm

408. Photograph   Mrs Minnie Baldock (*left*) and Mrs Coombes canvassing at a by-election, October 1907; 200mm × 230mm

409. Photograph   a suffragette addressing a large crowd, *c.* 1907; 200mm × 150mm

410. Photograph   a WSPU stall at Olympia, January 1908; 150mm × 200mm

411. Handbill   advertising a WSPU meeting in Trafalgar Square, 1 July 1906; 230mm × 150mm

412. Handbill   advertising a WSPU meeting in Victoria Park, 15 July 1906; 210mm × 140mm

413. Handbill   advertising a WSPU meeting in Hyde Park, 26 August 1906; 210mm × 140mm

414. Handbill   advertising a WSPU meeting in Finsbury Park, 28 October 1906; 220mm × 140mm

415. Ticket   for the 'Women's Parliament', Caxton Hall, 13 February 1907; 115mm × 78mm

416. Programme   for a NWSPU meeting, Queen's Hall, Langham Place, 11 November 1907; 150mm × 75mm

417. Programme   for a NWSPU meeting, Horticultural Hall, Westminster, 23 January 1908; 150mm × 80mm

418. Ticket   for a course of NWSPU lectures, Portman Rooms, Baker Street, 1908; 90mm × 115mm

419. Handbill   advertising 'Women's Sunday', 21 June 1908; 140mm × 250mm

420. Postcard   advertising a NWSPU meeting at Peckham Rye, 12 July 1908; 90mm × 140mm

421. Handbill   urging the public to go to the House of Commons on 13 October 1908, black on purple; 120mm × 190mm

422. Handbill   'Men and Women Help the Suffragettes to Rush the House of Commons', black on green, 13 October 1908; 200mm × 130mm

423. Handbill	'Men and Women Help the Suffragettes to Rush the House of Commons', black on manilla, 13 October 1908; 190mm × 130mm
424. Programme	for a 'Mass Meeting of Women', Albert Hall, 29 April 1909, with Sylvia Pankhurst's design of a woman scattering the seeds of women's suffrage, purple, white and green; 185mm × 120mm
425. Handbill	advertising WSPU 'At Homes' on 8 and 15 September 1909; 200mm × 130mm
426. Programme	for a WSPU 'Indignation Meeting', Albert Hall, 7 October 1909; 155mm × 100mm
427. Steward's ticket	for a WSPU meeting, Albert Hall, 9 December 1909; 115mm × 75mm
428. Handbill	advertising a NWSPU demonstration, Albert Hall, 9 December 1909, with Sylvia Pankhurst's 'angel' design, purple, white and green; 230mm × 150mm
429. Photograph	a suffragette advertising a meeting, closely scrutinised by four young boys, 1909; 170mm × 120mm
430. Programme	for Wimbledon WSPU's 'At Homes', 1910; 140mm × 90mm
431. Handbill	urging Irish women to take part in the WSPU 'monster demonstration', Hyde Park, 23 July 1910, green on white 150mm × 210mm
432. Handbill	advertising Wimbledon WSPU's meetings, 1911; 210mm × 150mm
433. Ticket	for a WSPU meeting, 4 Clement's Inn, 21 November 1911, black on purple; 75mm × 115mm
434. Handbill	urging the public to take part in the WSPU's 'Great Protest Meeting', Parliament Square, 4 March 1912; 220mm × 150mm
435. Ticket	for a WSPU reception, Connaught Rooms, Great Queen Street, 20 April 1912, with Sylvia Pankhurst's design of a woman scattering the seeds of women's suffrage, purple, white and green; 115mm × 150mm
436. Programme	for the WSPU 'Women's Demonstration', Albert Hall, 15 June 1912, purple on white; 155mm × 100mm

437. Ticket — for the WSPU 'Women's Demonstration', Albert Hall, 17 October 1912; 95mm × 115mm

438. Programme — for the WSPU's 'Women's Demonstration', Albert Hall, 17 October 1912; 150mm × 98mm

439. Advertisement — for free WSPU meetings for the public, London Pavilion, Piccadilly Circus, 1912; 155mm × 95mm

440. Ticket — for a WSPU meeting, London Pavilion, Piccadilly Circus, yellow, 21 July 1913; 115mm × 75mm

441. Ticket — for a WSPU meeting, Knightsbridge Hall, green, 20 October 1913; 80mm × 115mm

442. Programme — for the WSPU's 'Great Women's Demonstration at The Empress Theatre, Earl's Court Exhibition', purple, white and green, 7 December 1913; 210mm × 130mm

443. Ticket — for the WSPU's 'Great Women's Meeting', Holland Park Hall, 16 July 1914; 110mm × 70mm

'Deeds Not Words': getting arrested, street scenes and demonstrations

444. Photograph — police cordon at the end of Downing Street, 13 February 1908; 155mm × 160mm

445. Photograph — police outside 4 Clement's Inn waiting to arrest the WSPU leaders, Mrs Pankhurst, Miss Christabel Pankhurst and 'General' Flora Drummond, 13 October 1908 (the date on the photograph is incorrect); 100mm × 155mm

446. Photograph — Inspector Jarvis (centre) outside 4 Clement's Inn prior to arresting the WSPU leaders, 13 October 1908 (the date on the photograph is incorrect); 215mm × 145mm

447. Photograph	the arrest of Miss Olive Walton, *c.* 1910; 250mm × 200mm
448. Postcard	photograph of the arrest of Miss Grace Roe, 1914; 90mm × 140mm
449. Postcard	photograph, 'A Lancashire Lass in Clogs and Shawl being "Escorted" through Palace Yard', 16 October 1907; 90mm × 140mm
450. Photograph	'General' Flora Drummond (*left*), Mrs Pankhurst (*centre*) and Miss Christabel Pankhurst (*right*) being arrested at the WSPU's offices, Clement's Inn, 13 October 1908; 160mm × 220mm
451. Photograph	Mrs Pankhurst being presented with an emerald, pearl and amethyst necklace, Queen's Hall, Langham Place, 14 January 1909; 165mm × 210mm
452. Photograph	WSPU leaders addressing the meeting at Caxton Hall prior to the 'Rush the House of Commons' demonstration, 13 October 1908; 260mm × 310mm
453. Photograph	Mrs Mary Leigh (*left*) and Miss Edith New (the first WSPU window-smashers) on their release from Holloway Gaol, 22 August 1908; 160mm × 220mm
454. Photograph	Miss Daisy Dugdale in the 'suffragette uniform' leading the procession to welcome Mrs Pankhurst and Miss Christabel Pankhurst on their release from Holloway Gaol, 19 December 1908 (the date on the photograph is incorrect); 120mm × 160mm
455. Photograph	the Women's Band advertising the Women's Exhibition, May 1909; 120mm × 170mm
456. Photograph	Miss Daisy Dugdale leading the procession to welcome Mrs Pankhurst and Miss Christabel Pankhurst on their release from Holloway Gaol, 19 December 1908; 220mm × 150mm
457. Photograph	a suffragette procession welcoming Mrs Pankhurst and Miss Chistabel Pankhurst on their release from Holloway Gaol, 19 December 1908; 110mm × 155mm
458. Photograph	suffragettes advertising a deputation to the House of Commons, 30 June 1908; 180mm × 220mm (*Left to right*) Miss Dorothy Radcliffe, Miss Hilda Dallas, Miss Charlotte Marsh

459. Postcard   photograph of suffragettes walking to 'Women's Sunday' carrying a banner reading 'North Islington Women Demand the Vote', 21 June 1908; 90mm × 140mm

460. Photograph   Miss Dorothy Radcliffe leading a procession to Hyde Park, 21 June 1908; 150mm × 210mm

461. Photograph   a suffragette procession welcoming Miss Mary Phillips on her release from Holloway Gaol, 18 September 1908 (the date on the photograph is incorrect); 110mm × 160mm

462. Photograph   suffragettes marching from King's Cross to Tower Hill in honour of Mrs Mary Leigh and Mrs Gladys Evans who were on hunger-strike in Mountjoy Gaol, Dublin, 20 September 1912; 180mm × 250mm

463. Photograph   a suffragette accompanied by a male brass band advertising a meeting on 30 June 1909; 170mm × 120mm

464. Photograph   Miss Elsie Howey on horseback dressed as Joan of Arc, 19 April 1909; 200mm × 130mm

465. Photograph   suffragettes en route to 'Women's Sunday', 21 June 1908; 170mm × 110mm

466. Photograph   suffragettes campaigning at the Walthamstow by-election, 1909; 210mm × 180mm

467. Photograph   a suffragette procession, 7 October 1911; 210mm × 150mm

468. Photograph   a suffragette procession advertising several WSPU events, 19 April 1909; 130mm × 90mm

469. Photograph   a suffragette procession passing Portland Place, 1909; 230mm × 165mm

470. Photograph   a small crowd watching a suffragette procession passing Portland Place, 1909; 230mm × 160mm

471. Photograph   a police cordon and small crowd at the end of Downing Street, 1908; 150mm × 180mm

472. Photograph   suffragettes demonstrating at the end of Downing Street, several carrying placards decorated with convicts' arrows, 1912; 170mm × 220mm

Prisons and prisoners

473. Postcard   photograph of Holloway Gaol, c. 1912; 90mm × 140mm

474. Photograph   a landing in Holloway Gaol, c. 1910   120mm × 170mm

475. Photograph   Mrs Pankhurst (*left*) and Miss Christabel Pankhurst dressed in replica prison clothing after their release from Holloway Gaol, December 1908; 150mm × 110mm

476. Postcard   photograph of two suffragettes dressed in replica prison clothing as a warder and a prisoner, standing in front of a mock cell door, 1908; 90mm × 140mm

477. Photograph   reconstruction of a cell at Holloway Gaol, c. 1909; 110mm × 120mm

478. Photograph   reconstruction of a cell at Holloway Gaol, showing the bed, c. 1909; 140mm × 155mm

479. Postcard   photograph of Miss Katharine Gatty dressed in replica prison clothing, January 1913; 90mm × 140mm

480. Postcard   Lady Constance Lytton wearing two hunger-strike medals, c. 1912; 90mm × 140mm

481. Photograph   Mrs Pankhurst (*left*), 'General' Flora Drummond (*centre*) and Miss Christabel Pankhurst (*right*) in the dock at Bow Street Magistrates' Court, 21–22 October 1908; 120mm × 165mm

482. Postcard   Mrs Pankhurst (*left*), 'General' Flora Drummond (*centre*) and Miss Christabel Pankhurst (*right*) in the dock at Bow Street Magistrates' Court, 21–22 October 1908; 90mm × 140mm

483. Photograph   a suffragette exercising in the yard at Holloway Gaol, c. 1910; 100mm × 60mm

484. Photograph   four suffragettes exercising in the yard at Holloway Gaol, c. 1910; 70mm × 90mm

485. Photograph   a suffragette exercising in the yard at Holloway Gaol, c. 1910; 150mm × 65mm

486. Postcard	woodcut, 'The English Inquisitors Have Revived Torture in Our Prisons', *c.* 1912; 90mm × 140mm
Hooded figures surround a coffin bearing a hero's sword

487. Newspaper	*The Suffragette*, loose copy, WSPU, 6 February 1914; 380mm × 265mm

488. Pamphlet	*The Trial of the Suffragette Leaders*, The Woman's Press, 1908; 220mm × 150mm

489. Pamphlet	*Forcible Feeding – A Letter to a Liberal Member of Parliament*, December 1909; 290mm × 220mm

490. Book	*Roll of Honour of Suffragette Prisoners 1905–1914*, handwritten, green cover, purple, white and green illustration in text, privately published, 1914; 280mm × 230mm

491. Pamphlet	*Holloway Jingles*, ed. N.A. John, Glasgow WSPU, 1912; 180mm × 110mm

492. Pamphlet	*Concerning the Status of Political Prisoners*, W. Lyon Blease, *c.* 1913; 220mm × 150mm

493. Handbill	advertising a demonstration by Anglican clergy at Queen's Hall, Langham Place, W1, 5 December 1913, to protest against force-feeding, Utopia Press; 220mm × 270mm

494. Pamphlet	*Tortured Women – What Forcible Feeding Means*, WSPU, 1914; 270mm × 210mm

495. Handbill	advertising a demonstration by Anglican clergy at Queen's Hall, Langham Place, W1, 5 December 1913, to protest against force-feeding; 220mm × 140mm

496. Photograph	breakfast party to welcome Mrs Pankhurst and Miss Christabel Pankhurst at the Inns of Court Hotel, 22 December 1908; 115mm × 155mm
(*Left to right*) Miss Annie Kenney, Miss Sylvia Pankhurst, Mrs Pankhurst, Mrs Emmeline Pethick-Lawrence, Miss Mary Gawthorpe, Miss Adela Pankhurst

497. Photograph	the first prisoners' breakfast party, 20 October 1905; 160mm × 210mm
(*Left to right*) Mrs Minnie Baldock, Miss Christabel Pankhurst, Miss Annie Kenney, Mrs Martel

498. Knife	smuggled out of Holloway Gaol, *c.* 1912; 190mm × 40mm

499. Figurine of a suffragette	clay from the exercise yard at Holloway Gaol, with box, c. 1912; 70mm × 20mm *By permission of the Fawcett Library, City of London Polytechnic*
500. Two Holloway brooches	silver, with Sylvia Pankhurst's design of a convict's arrow in purple, white and green enamel on a silver portcullis, awarded to suffragettes who went to prison for their involvement in the WSPU campaign, c. 1908; 20mm × 25mm
501. Towel	linen, smuggled out of Holloway Gaol, c. 1912; 440mm × 660mm
502. Socks	wool, knitted in Holloway Gaol, black with red stripes, c. 1912; 150mm × 40mm
503. Bag	cotton, with convict's arrow design appliquéd in cotton thread, made in Holloway Gaol, blue and white, c. 1912; 135mm × 130mm
504. Handkerchief case	linen, with 'Grace', 'Holloway' and 'March 1912' embroidered in green silk, made in Holloway Gaol, 1912; 430mm × 130mm
505. Bowl	wood, smuggled out of Holloway Gaol by Miss Jane Terrero, 1912; 75mm × 40mm
506. Hunger-strike medal	silver, attached to a purple, white and green silk ribbon, awarded to Miss Florence Haig, three bars engraved with the dates of her force-feeding, 1912; 120mm × 40mm *(From the top)* 1 March 1912, 4 months 1 July 1908, 3 months 12 February 1908, 6 weeks
507. Badge	numbered DX 2/7, metal alloy, attached to a purple, white and green silk ribbon, awarded to Mrs Helena Tyson for her prison sentence, 1909; 70mm × 60mm Engraved on the reverse: 'February 24 to March 24 1909 . . . In remembrance . . . a token of admiration and affection from the New Union'
508. Badge	numbered DX 3/31, metal alloy, attached to a purple, white and green silk ribbon, awarded to Miss Diana Katrina Tyson for her prison sentence, 1909; 70mm × 60mm Engraved on the reverse: 'In remembrance of February 24 to March 24 1909, a token of affection from the New Union'

509. Badge	numbered DX 2/32, metal alloy, awarded to Miss Leonora Tyson for her prison sentence, 1912; 40mm × 30mm Engraved on the reverse: 'In remembrance of March 9 to May 8 1912, a token of appreciation from the Streatham WSPU'
510. Photograph	suffragettes wearing tartan shawls and carrying Scottish flowers welcome Miss Mary Phillips (*middle row, third from left*), a Scottish suffragette, on her release from Holloway Gaol, September 1908; 220mm × 270mm
511. Photograph	a suffragette procession to welcome Mrs Jennie Baines in Trafalgar Square after her release from Armley Gaol, Leeds, 12 December 1908; 170mm × 220mm
512. Prison rules	for convicted prisoners, *c.* 1908; 350mm × 200mm
513. Pamphlet	*Roll of Honour – Suffragette Prisoners 1905–1914*, 1914; 250mm × 180mm
514. Handbill	'Five Days in a Dungeon: Suffragette's Holloway Experiences', Florence E. Cooke, *c.* 1914; 290mm × 220mm
515. Handbill	'Treatment of the Suffragettes in Prison', F.W. Pethick-Lawrence, The Woman's Press, *c.* 1910; 300mm × 210mm
516. Pamphlet	*Suffrage Speeches from the Dock*, The Woman's Press, 1912; 220mm × 150mm
517. Programme	'Public Breakfast', for suffragettes released from Holloway Gaol, Eustace Miles Restaurant, Chandos Street, Covent Garden, 3 April 1907; 90mm × 100mm
518. Licence	releasing Miss Gertrude Mary Ansell from prison under the Prisoner's Temporary Discharge for Ill-Health Act ('The Cat and Mouse Act'), 6 August 1913; 320mm × 180mm
519. Textile	silk, embroidered with the signatures of women in Holloway Gaol in March 1912, purple, white and green silk ribbon border, with a postcard photograph of Mrs Pankhurst and Miss Christabel Pankhurst; 515mm × 450mm
520. Photograph	suffragettes taking Mrs Mary Leigh and Miss Edith New to Queen's Hall, Langham Place, W1, August 1908; 160mm × 210mm

521. Photograph   Mrs Pankhurst (*left*) and Miss Christabel Pankhurst being driven in a landau to a 'Welcome Breakfast' at the Inns of Court Hotel, 22 December 1908; 165mm × 220mm

522. Photograph   suffragettes welcoming Miss Patricia Woodlock on her release from prison, 16 June 1909 (the date on the photograph is incorrect); 160mm × 210mm

523. Photograph   Miss Patricia Woodlock on her release from prison, 16 June 1909 (the date on the photograph is incorrect); 115mm × 160mm

524. Letter   on prison lavatory paper, written to Miss Ada Flatman by Mrs Mary Leigh in Holloway Gaol, 1908; nine pieces, each 150mm × 110mm

525. Telegram   informing relatives of Mrs Arncliffe Sennett's arrest for using 'threatening language', 21 November 1911; 210mm × 170mm

526. Metropolitan Police charge sheet   charging Miss Jane Terrero to appear at Bow Street for causing wilful damage (smashing windows), 1 March 1912; 200mm × 250mm

527. Programme   for a 'Social Evening', Suffolk Street Galleries, Pall Mall, purple on green, 21 January 1911; 230mm × 150mm

528. Handbill   'The Case of Mrs Pankhurst – A Victim of the "Cat and Mouse Act"', WSPU, *c.* 1913; 300mm × 210mm

529. Handbill   'Forcible Feeding in Prison – Opinions of Medical Experts', *c.* 1912; 309mm × 210mm

530. Photograph   suffragettes waiting outside Bow Street Magistrates' Court for the trial of Mrs Pankhurst, Miss Christabel Pankhurst and 'General' Flora Drummond, October 1908 (the date on the photograph is incorrect); 170mm × 220mm

531. Photograph   Scottish suffragettes welcoming Miss Mary Phillips on her release from Holloway Gaol, September 1908; 110mm × 140mm

532. Postcard   photograph of Mrs Pankhurst and Miss Christabel Pankhurst after a breakfast party at the Inns of Court Hotel, 22 December 1908; 150mm × 120mm

533. Photograph   Mrs Mary Leigh (*left*) and Miss Edith New (*holding flowers*) on their release from Holloway Gaol, August 1908 (the date on the photograph is incorrect); 120mm × 150mm

534. Pamphlet   *The Medical Aspects of Forcible Feeding*, c. 1914; 260mm × 180mm

535. Postcard   photograph of Mrs Pankhurst's 'Cat and Mouse' licence, July 1913; 90mm × 140mm

536. Newspaper   *The Suffragette*, loose copy, WSPU, 25 July 1913; 38mm × 265mm

537. Illuminated scroll   paper, awarded to Miss Elsa Gye for her prison sentence, designed by Sylvia Pankhurst, 1908; 320mm × 500mm

The Conciliation Bill

538. Photograph   a WSPU rally in support of the Conciliation Bill, with men holding a banner saying 'Where There's a Bill There's a Way', July 1910; 210mm × 160mm

539. Book   *Book of Parliamentary Debates*, House of Commons, vol. xix, no. 72, 11 July 1910, HMSO, 1910; 250mm × 165mm

540. Postcard   cartoon, 'The Vote Girl', c. 1911; 90mm × 140mm
A boy and girl have a tug-of-war with the Conciliation Bill: 'I want the Vote, and I mean to have the Vote, that's the sort of Girl I am.'

541. Pamphlet   *The 'Conciliation' Bill: An Explanation and Defence*, H.N. Brailsford, Garden City Press, c. 1911; 220mm × 140mm

542. Photograph   a WSPU rally in Hyde Park in support of the Conciliation Bill, July 1910; 130mm × 210mm

543. Pamphlet   *Treatment of the Women's Deputation of November 18, 22 and 23, 1910*, The Woman's Press, 1913; 185mm × 120mm

544. Photograph   WSPU meeting in Caxton Hall before the 'Black Friday' riot at the House of Commons, 18 November 1910; 120mm × 170mm

545. Photograph	the large police presence at the House of Commons on 'Black Friday', 18 November 1910; 120mm × 165mm
546. Photograph	a suffragette struggling with a policeman on 'Black Friday', 18 November 1910; 120mm × 170mm

The Women's Coronation Procession, 17 June 1911

547. Handbill	urging Irish women to go to the Women's Coronation Procession, 17 June 1911; 220mm × 150mm
548. Handbill	advertising the Women's Coronation Procession, purple, white and green, 17 June 1911; 260mm × 160mm
549. Souvenir programme	for the Women's Coronation Procession, 17 June 1911, The Woman's Press, 1911; 220mm × 280mm
550. Photograph	members of the Actresses' Franchise League and their banner at the Women's Coronation Procession, 17 June 1911; 135mm × 220mm
551. Banner	cotton sateen, with appliquéd pink silk embroidery and green and gold paint, Actresses' Franchise League, c. 1911; 2000mm × 1022mm
552. Postcard	photograph of suffragettes (many ex-prisoners) carrying convicts' arrow staves at the Women's Coronation Procession, 17 June 1911; 90mm × 140mm
553. Postcard	photograph of Miss Annan Bryce on horseback dressed as Joan of Arc leading the Women's Coronation Procession, 17 June 1911; 90mm × 140mm
554. Photograph	'Prison to Citizenship' banner, the Women's Coronation Procession, 17 June 1911; 210mm × 170mm
555. Photograph	suffragettes 'forming up' at the Women's Coronation Procession, (centre right) Lady Constance Lytton, 17 June 1911; 230mm × 160mm

556. Photograph the musicians' section of the Actresses' Franchise League and their banner at the Women's Coronation Procession, 17 June 1911; 220mm × 170mm

557. Photograph Welsh suffragettes in traditional costume at the Women's Coronation Procession, 17 June 1911; 160mm × 150mm

558. Photograph the 'Famous Women' contingent of the Women's Coronation Procession, 17 June 1911; 240mm × 160mm

559. Photograph 'The Car of Empire' at the Women's Coronation Procession, 17 June 1911; 220mm × 170mm

560. Postcard photograph of the 'Prison to Citizenship' banner at the Women's Coronation Procession, 17 June 1911; 90mm × 140mm

561. Photograph 'The Car of Empire' at the Women's Coronation Procession, 17 June 1911; 190mm × 260mm

562. Photograph Indian suffragettes at the Women's Coronation Procession, 17 June 1911; 220mm × 150mm

563. Postcard photograph of Welsh suffragettes in traditional costume at the Women's Coronation Procession, 17 June 1911; 90mm × 140mm

'Rise Up Women!': the escalation of militancy

564. Handbill 'Window Breaking. To One Who Has Suffered', The Woman's Press, 1912; 300mm × 210mm

565. Handbill 'Broken Windows', Christabel Pankhurst, The Woman's Press, 1912; 300mm × 210mm

566. Photograph broken windows at an Aerated Bread Company shop, 1 March 1912; 190mm × 160mm

567. Photograph	the first window-smashers, Mrs Mary Leigh (*left*) and Miss Edith New, in the dock at Bow Street Magistrates Court, June 1908; 120mm × 170mm
568. Photograph	a portrait of Thomas Carlyle damaged at the National Portrait Gallery, 1914; 200mm × 150mm
569. Photograph	'Slasher Mary' Richardson, who attacked *The Rokeby Venus* at the National Gallery in March 1914, leaving court, 1914; 135mm × 180mm
570. Photograph	the WSPU's offices at Lincoln's Inn House raided by the police, May 1913; 160mm × 210mm
571. Photograph	Lady White's house burnt down by suffragettes, 20 March 1913; 150mm × 120mm
572. Photograph	'The Capture of The Monument' by suffragettes, 18 April 1913; 170mm × 220mm
573. Photograph	the house of Mr Arthur du Cros, MP at St Leonard's, Hastings, burnt down by suffragettes, April 1913; 160mm × 210mm
574. Photograph	five suffragettes holding a broken window in its frame (*far left* Miss Adela Pankhurst), *c.* 1912; 170mm × 110mm
575. Catapult	metal and leather, used to break windows, *c.* 1912; 280mm × 100mm
576. Photograph	a building wrecked by suffragettes, *c.* 1913; 200mm × 150mm
577. Padded cosh	leather, the handle bound with purple, white and green ribbon, *c.* 1913; 400mm × 50mm
578. Two metal discs	put in letterboxes during a raid on GPO property, *c.* 1913; diameter 20mm
579. Penny	defaced with 'Votes For Women', *c.* 1912; diameter 30mm
580. Photograph	Rusholme Exhibition Centre, Manchester, wrecked by suffragettes, December 1913; 150mm × 120mm
581. Cricket ball	thrown through the Home Secretary's window, 1914 *By permission of John Kennedy Melling*

582. Toffee-hammer   wood and leather, broken, used for smashing windows, *c.* 1912; 290mm × 15mm × 40mm (at the widest point)

583. Photograph   David Lloyd George's new house in Surrey damaged by suffragettes, February 1913; 150mm × 110mm

584. Postcard   photograph of Wargrave church, attacked by suffragette arsonists, 1 June 1914; 90mm × 140mm

585. Photograph   a church burnt down by suffragettes, 6 May 1913; 180mm × 140mm

Men's involvement

586. Postcard   photograph of John Stuart Mill, probably taken in the 1880s, *c.* 1909; 90mm × 140mm

587. Postcard   photograph of Mr Victor Duval, Honorary Organising Secretary of the Men's Political Union for Women's Enfranchisement (MPUWE), *c.* 1912; 90mm × 140mm

588. Postcard   photograph of Mr Philip Snowden, MP, *c.* 1913; 90mm × 140mm

589. Postcard   photograph of Mr Hugh A. Franklin (MPUWE), *c.* 1913; 90mm × 140mm

590. Postcard   photograph of Mr George Lansbury, MP, *c.* 1910; 80mm × 135mm

591. Postcard   photograph of the arrest of Captain C.M. Gonne (MPUWE), 18 November 1910; 90mm × 140mm

592. Newspaper   *Men's League for Women's Suffrage Monthly Paper*, bound volume, 1909–1914; 310mm × 250mm

593. Newspaper   *Men's League for Women's Suffrage Monthly Paper*, loose copy, January 1910; 320mm × 240mm

594. Newspaper   *Men's League for Women's Suffrage Monthly Paper*, loose copy, November 1910; 320mm × 240mm

595. Book	*The Subjection of Women*, John Stuart Mill, Longmans, Green & Co., new impression, 1911; 190mm × 120mm
596. Book	*Woman Suffrage*, Arnold Harris Mathew, T.C. Jack and E.C. Jack, 1907; 200mm × 140mm
597. Pamphlet	*Women's Suffrage: The Demand and Its Meaning*, Robert F. Cholmeley, T. Fisher Unwin, 1907; 180mm × 120mm
598. Pamphlet	*Women's Suffrage and the Social Evil*, Revd R.J. Campbell, Women's Freedom League, 1907; 220mm × 140mm
599. Badge	tin, Men's League for Women's Suffrage, black on yellow, c. 1910; diameter 25mm
600. Membership card	Men's League for Women's Suffrage, c. 1910; 60mm × 90mm
601. Pamphlet	*The Earl of Lytton on Votes For Women*, a speech delivered at St James's Theatre, 15 June 1909, The Woman's Press, 1909; 220mm × 145mm
602. Pamphlet	*The Citizenship of Women: A Plea for Women's Suffrage*, J. Keir Hardie, MP, Independent Labour Party, 4th ed., 1906; 210mm × 140mm
603. Pamphlet	*Sex-War and Woman's Suffrage: A Lecture given by Laurence Housman at The Large Essex Hall* (Essex Street, Strand). Women's Freedom League, 7 May 1912; 170mm × 95mm
604. Pamphlet	*The Men's League Handbook on Women's Suffrage*, Men's League for Women's Suffrage, 1913; 130mm × 190mm
605. Report	*Sixth Annual Report of the Men's League for Women's Suffrage*, April 1913; 220mm × 140mm
606. Pamphlet	*The Emancipation of Woman, A Lecture by A Mere Man*, printed in Trinidad, 1907; 210mm × 140mm

Deputation to see the King, 21 May 1914

607. Handbill

'To Buckingham Palace', illustration by Hilda Dallas, purple, white and green, May 1914; 290mm × 210mm

608. Photograph

policemen running towards suffragettes at the gates of Buckingham Palace, 21 May 1914; 120mm × 170mm

609. Photograph

crowds watching the suffragette deputation attempt to enter Buckingham Palace, 21 May 1914; 290mm × 210mm

Outbreak of the First World War and the Vote

610. Book

The Reform Act of 1918, Liberal Publication Department, 1918; 210mm × 135mm

611. Postcard

'At Last!', drawing of Joan of Arc holding a 'Woman's Franchise' flag, taken from *Punch*, 23 January 1918; 90mm × 140mm

Personal testimony

612. Book

Memories of a Militant, Annie Kenney, purple, white and green cover, Edward Arnold and Co., 1924; 230mm × 150mm

613. Book

The Suffragette: History of the Women's Militant Suffrage Movement 1905–1910, E. Sylvia Pankhurst, with Sylvia Pankhurst's portcullis design in silver, purple, white and green on a purple cover, Gay and Hancock, 1911; 195mm × 135mm

614. Book

The Hard Way Up: The Autobiography of Hannah Mitchell, Suffragette and Rebel, ed. Geoffrey Mitchell, Faber and Faber, 1968; 210mm × 140mm

615. Book

My Own Story, Emmeline Pankhurst, Eveleigh Nash, 1914; 230mm × 150mm

616. Book	*Put Up Thy Sword*, Adela Pankhurst, Women's Peace Army, 1915; 190mm × 130mm
617. Book	*Fate Has Been Kind*, Frederick Pethick-Lawrence, Hutchinson, 1943; 230mm × 150mm
618. Book	*My Part in a Changing World*, Emmeline Pethick-Lawrence, Victor Gollancz, 1938; 240mm × 150mm
619. Pamphlet	*Memories of Charlotte Marsh*, Suffragette Fellowship, June 1961; 220mm × 140mm
620. Book	*A Suffragette's Love-Letters*, anon, Chatto and Windus, 1907; 190mm × 130mm
621. Book	*Prisons and Prisoners: Some Personal Experiences*, Constance Lytton and Jane Warton, with Sylvia Pankhurst's design of a woman emerging from captivity and stepping over chains in purple, white and green, on a purple cover, William Heinemann, 1914; 190mm × 130mm
622. Book	*Laugh a Defiance*, Mary A. Richardson, Weidenfeld & Nicholson, 1953, 220mm × 150mm
623. Pamphlet	*How I Became A Suffragette*, A.M. Wright, privately published, c. 1920; 220mm × 140mm
624. Newsletter	*Calling All Women*, Suffragette Fellowship, February 1966; 250mm × 210mm
625. Newsletter	*Calling All Women*, Suffragette Fellowship, February 1969; 250mm × 210mm

Pageant and parade

| 626. Poster | 'Women Need the Vote: Only Those who Elect Parliament have Power to Make it Serve Them', c. 1912; 750mm × 1000mm
A woman seated beneath an arch ('Political Power'), with 'Women's Interests' and 'Crowded Out' |

627. Poster   'Modern Chivalry', colour c. 1910; 750mm × 1000mm
A medieval knight on a white charger, holding a sword ('Votes'),
comes to the rescue of a fair damsel holding a pennant ('Justice')

628. Poster   'Welcome Christabel Pankhurst', advertising *Votes for Women*, purple,
white and green, 17 December 1908; 700mm × 500mm

629. Poster   'The Appeal of Womanhood', Louise Jacobs, colour, 1912;
920mm × 700mm
A woman holding a scroll ('Our Message to Women of all Nations – Dare
to be Free') stands in front of a group of cowed and miserable women

630. Poster   'In the Shadow', c. 1913; 850mm × 700mm
In the brightness of the 'Franchise Light', men present their petitions to
government, whereas women sweated workers languish in the dark,
gloomy shadows

631. Poster   cartoon, 'The Prehistoric Argument', Catherine Courtauld, colour, 1912;
1150mm × 760mm
A Stone Age couple stand at the door of their cave, No. 1, Cavern Villas.
Primeval woman : 'Why can't I go out too and see the world?'
Primeval man : 'Because you can't. Woman's proper sphere is the Cave.'

632. Poster   'Factory Acts', Emily Ford, colour, 1908; 1020mm × 750mm
A female mill-worker stands at a door bearing the sign 'Factory Acts –
Regulations for Women' : 'They Have a Cheek. I've Never Been Ask[ed]'

633. Poster   'The Modern Inquisition', Alfred Pearse ('A Patriot'), colour, 1910;
750mm × 480mm
A suffragette is held down and force-fed by a prison doctor and four
wardresses

634. Poster   'St Helena for Malignant Suffragettes', *Daily Express*, 8 May (?)1914;
780mm × 550mm

Banners and banner-making

635. Photograph	suffragettes carrying banners to a rally in Hyde Park, July 1910; 170mm × 110mm
636. Photograph	Mrs Arncliffe Sennett carrying the 'Victoria Queen and Mother' banner (see **649**), 13 June 1908; 300mm × 250mm
637. Photograph	suffragettes making banners and pennants, 23 July 1910; 210mm × 160mm
638. Pamphlet	*Banners and Banner-Making*, Mary Lowndes, September 1909 (temporarily removed from Mary Lowndes's sketchbook); 220mm × 140mm *By permission of the Fawcett Library, City of London Polytechnic*
639. Watercolour design and fabric samples	for the 'Boadicea' banner (see **644**), Mary Lowndes, 1908 (temporarily removed from Mary Lowndes's sketchbook); design 10mm × 130mm, fabric samples 40mm × 110mm *By permission of the Fawcett Library, City of London Polytechnic*
640. Watercolour design and fabric samples	for the 'Holloway' banner, Mary Lowndes, c. 1910 (temporarily removed from Mary Lowndes's sketchbook); design 120mm × 20mm, fabric samples 80mm × 160mm *By permission of the Fawcett Library, City of London Polytechnic*
641. Watercolour design	for the 'Marie Curie' banner (see **301**), probably by Mary Lowndes, c. 1908 (temporarily removed from Mary Lowndes's sketchbook); 110mm × 750mm *By permission of the Fawcett Library, City of London Polytechnic*
642. Banner	'Victory', cotton, painted purple, white and green (faded), c. 1914; 730mm × 610mm Chief Inspector Rolfe confiscated this banner on 21 May 1914 from Mrs Pankhurst, who told him it was made from her 'nether garments' (it contains a piece of whalebone) *By permission of the Metropolitan Police Museum*
643. Flag	linen, three panels sewn together, purple, white and green, now attached to a copper pole, 1913; 1140mm × 700mm Reputedly wrapped round Emily Wilding Davison when she made her protest at the Derby

644. Banner

'Boadicea', moiré silk, velveteen, silk, wool, cotton, woollen tassels and metal braid, designed by Mary Lowndes, 1908; 1270mm × 900mm
Shield-shaped, with 'Boadicea' painted in gold on cream silk, orange circular motif and daggers in appliqué, and fleurs-de-lis painted in gold

645. Banner

'Home-makers Demand Votes', cotton, silk, satin, wool and metal braid, designed by Mary Lowndes, 1908; 1600mm × 940mm
Home-makers in yellow satin edged with metal braid above an appliquéd lamp and the words 'Remember their Homeless Sisters' in braid; 'Women's Suffrage' crudely painted on the reverse

646. Banner

'Young Women's Christian Association', linen, silk, cotton twill and metal braid, multi-coloured, c. 1911; 1020mm × 920mm
'YWCA', 'Overseas Friends', 'Africa', 'China', 'Egypt', 'Palestine', 'Japan' and 'India' in appliqué and a ship outlined in silk thread

647. Banner

'West Ham', velvet and silk, purple, white and green, West Ham WSPU, c. 1912; 1200mm × 1700mm
Sylvia Pankhurst's 'angel' design, with 'West Ham', 'Courage' 'Constancy' and 'Success' in appliqué

648. Banner

'MSPU', cotton, cotton twill and ribbon, purple, white and green, c. 1911; 1480mm × 2420mm
The convict's arrow, 'MSPU', 'City Temple', 'GNR Bradford', '33 Eccleston Square' and 'Downing Street' in embroidery
('MSPU' is confusing: it could be 'WSPU' or it could relate to a men's group)

649. Banner

'Victoria Queen and Mother', velvet and metal braid, designed by Mary Lowndes, 1908; 1440mm × 1040mm
Shield-shaped, with cloth of gold letters spelling 'Victoria Queen and Mother' and three gold lions edged in metal braid on deep pink velvet background

650. Banner

'Ask With Courage', cotton sateen, purple and white, c. 1908; 1130mm × 2420mm
White letters on purple background spelling 'Ask With Courage'

651. Banner

'Chelsea', painted cotton, designed by Herman Ross, colour, Chelsea WSPU, 1908; 1080 × 840mm
Two burly policemen outside Holloway Gaol and a suffragette waving a flag with the motto 'Votes For Women' from one of the windows

652. Banner	satinette, damask, velvet and tassels, purple, white and green, Hammersmith WSPU, c. 1911; 2180mm (overall width) × 960mm 'Hammer Smith' and 'Deeds Not Words' appliquéd above a central panel of three hammers and horseshoes painted on fabric over card; side panels of irises, embroidered on one side and appliquéd on the other, to ensure the design's reversibility
653. Banner	black paint on white canvas, c. 1908; 1160mm × 840mm Handcuffs, a padlock and a metal chain (inserted into the hemmed edges) have been added to this banner, advertising a meeting at the Albert Hall
654. Two flags	silk, three panels sewn together, purple, white and green, c. 1908; 1400mm × 690mm
655. Three pennants	satin, pink and green (the colours of the Actresses' Franchise League), attached to wooden sticks, c. 1911; 790mm × 360mm With the names of the actresses 'Agnes Larkcom', 'Emily Pertwee' and 'Ada Moore' painted in black
656. Banner	'Holloway Prisoners', linen, purple, white and green, c. 1910; 2270mm × 2200mm With the signatures of 80 Holloway hunger-strikers embroidered in purple silk; at the top are the words 'Women's Social and Political Union' and the names 'Mrs P. Lawrence', 'Cristabel' (mis-spelt), 'Mrs Pankhurst' and 'Annie Kennie' (mis-spelt)

Supplementary items

The following objects have been used to help evoke the period of the suffragette campaign.

Tradesman's cart	two-wheeled, as used by London butchers and sweeps, early to mid-19th century
Lady's bicycle	c. 1900 *By permission of the Science Museum*

Woman's suit	raw silk, cream-yellow, trimmed with black silk satin and cream silk braid, label from Green & Edwards Ltd, Finchley Road, NW, 1908–12
Hat	plaited black fibre trimmed with iridescent glass beads, 1912–14
Dress	linen, white, decorated with tucks, openwork and handmade buttons, with ribbed green and pink sash (the colours of the Actresses' Franchise League), 1910–14
Hat	plaited natural straw trimmed with black velvet ribbon and pleated crimson muslin (the rose is modern), label from Robert Heath, 37/39 Knightsbridge, SW, 1909–12
Dress	cotton voile, mauve and white striped, with embroidered cotton collar, 1910–12
Office furniture and equipment	including Bentwood chairs, typewriter, firebucket, writing table, cash register, wooden filing cabinet, umbrella stand, embosser, clock, hatstand, customer receipt box, ink fountain pens, notebook, paper fastener
Newspapers	bound volumes and loose copies of *Votes For Women* and *The Suffragette*

BIBLIOGRAPHY

ADAM, 1975

R. Adam, *A Woman's Place, 1910–75*, Chatto and Windus, 1975

ADAMS, 1982

C. Adams, *Ordinary Lives*, Virago, 1982

ALBERTI, 1989

J. Alberti, *Beyond Suffrage: Feminists in War and Peace, 1914–1928*, Macmillan, 1989

ATKINSON, 1986

D. Atkinson, *Votes For Women* (document pack), Elm Publications, 1986

ATKINSON, 1988

D. Atkinson, *Suffragettes*, HMSO, 1988

ATKINSON, 1988

D. Atkinson, *Votes For Women*, Cambridge University Press, 1988

ATKINSON, 1988

D. Atkinson, *Mrs Broom's Suffragette Photographs*, Nishen Photography, 1988

BARNES, 1980

A. Barnes, *Tough Annie: From Suffragette to Stepney Councillor*, Stepney Books, 1980

BEDDOE, 1989

D. Beddoe, *Back to Home and Duty*, Pandora, 1989

BILLINGTON, 1982

R. Billington, 'Ideology and Feminism: Why the Suffragettes were "Wild Women"', *Women's Studies International Forum*, vol.v, no.6, 1982

BILLINGTON-GREIG, 1987

T. Billington-Greig, *The Non-Violent Militant: Selected Writings of Teresa Billington-Greig*, eds Carol McPhee and Ann Fitzgerald, Routledge & Kegan Paul, 1987

CAINE, 1982

B. Caine, 'Feminism, Suffrage and the Nineteenth-Century English Women's Movement', *Women's Studies International Forum*, vol.v, no.6, 1982

CASTLE, 1987

B. Castle, *Sylvia and Christabel Pankhurst*, Penguin, 1987

CLOSE, 1977

D. Close, 'The Collapse of Resistance to Democracy: Conservatives, Adult Suffrage and Second Chamber Reform, 1911–1928', *Historical Journal*, vol.xx, no.4, 1977

DANGERFIELD, 1966

G. Dangerfield, *The Strange Death of Liberal England*, Paladin, 1966

ENGLANDER, 1992

S. Englander, *Class Conflict and Class Coalition in the California Woman Suffrage Movement 1907–1912*, Edwin Mellen Press, 1992

FULFORD, 1958

R. Fulford, *Votes For Women*, Faber & Faber, 1958

GARNER, 1984

L. Garner, *Stepping Stones to Women's Freedom: Feminist Ideas in the Women's Suffrage Movement, 1900–18*, Heinemann, 1984

GARRETT FAWCETT, 1920

M. Garrett Fawcett, *The Women's Victory and After: Personal Reminiscences 1911–18*, Sidgwick & Jackson, 1920

GARRETT FAWCETT, 1924

M. Garrett Fawcett, *What I Remember*, T. Fisher Unwin, 1924

HARRISON, 1978

B. Harrison, *Separate Spheres: The Opposition to Women's Suffrage in Britain*, Croom Helm, 1978

HARRISON, 1983

B. Harrison, 'Women's Suffrage at Westminster, 1866–1928', in *High and Low Politics in Modern Britain*, eds M. Bentley and J. Stevenson, Oxford University Press, 1983

HARRISON, 1987

B. Harrison, *Prudent Revolutionaries*, Clarendon Press, 1987

HART, 1889

H. Hart, *Women's Suffrage and the National Danger*, 1889

HOLLEDGE, 1981

J. Holledge, *Innocent Flowers: Women in the Edwardian Theatre*, Virago, 1981

HOLLIS, 1975

P. Hollis, *Women in Public: The Women's Movement, 1850–1900*, Allen & Unwin, 1975

HOLTON, 1986

S.S. Holton, *Feminism and Democracy: Women's Suffrage and Reform Politics in Britain, 1900–1918*, Cambridge University Press, 1986

KAMM, 1966

J. Kamm, *Rapiers and Battleaxes*, Allen & Unwin, 1966

KAZANTZIS, 1967

J. Kazantzis, *Women in Revolt*, Jonathan Cape, 1967

KENNEY, 1924

A. Kenney, *Memories of a Militant*, Edward Arnold, 1924

KENT, 1987

S. Kingsley Kent, *Sex and Suffrage in Britain, 1860–1914*, Princeton, 1987

KOSS, 1976

S. Koss, *Asquith*, Hamish Hamilton, 1976

KRADITOR, 1981

A.S. Kraditor, *The Ideas of the Woman Suffrage Movement, 1890–1920*, W. W. Norton, 1981

KRAMER, 1988

A. Kramer, *How they Lived: A Suffragette*, Wayland, 1988

LENEMAN, 1991

L. Leneman, *'A Guid Cause': The Women's Suffrage Movement in Scotland*, Aberdeen University Press, 1991

LEVENSON, 1983

L. Levenson, *With Wooden Sword: A Biography of Francis Sheehy Skeffington*, Arlen House, 1983

LEVENSON, 1985

L. Levenson, *In Her Own Right: A Biography of Hanna Sheehy Skeffington*, Arlen House, 1985

LEWIS, G., 1988

G. Lewis, *Eva Gore-Booth and Esther Roper*, Pandora, 1988

LEWIS, J., 1973

J. Lewis, 'Beyond Suffrage: English Feminism in the 1920s', *Maryland Historian*, 1973

LEWIS, J., 1987

J. Lewis (ed.), *Before the Vote was Won: Arguments For and Against Women's Suffrage, 1864–1896*, Routledge & Kegan Paul, 1987

LIDDINGTON & NORRIS, 1978

J. Liddington and J. Norris, *One Hand Tied Behind Us: The Rise of the Women's Suffrage Movement*, Virago, 1978

LIDDINGTON, 1983

J. Liddington, 'The Women's Peace Crusade', in *Over Our Dead Bodies*, ed. D. Thompson, Virago, 1983

LIDDINGTON, 1984

J. Liddington, *The Life and Times of a Respectable Rebel: Selina Cooper 1864–1946*, Virago, 1984

LINKLATER, 1980

A. Linklater, *An Unhusbanded Life*, Hutchinson, 1980

MACKENZIE, 1975

M. Mackenzie, *Shoulder to Shoulder: A Documentary*, Penguin, 1975

MARCUS, 1987

J. Marcus (ed.), *Suffrage and the Pankhursts*, Routledge & Kegan Paul, 1987

MARWICK, 1977

A. Marwick, *Women at War*, Fontana, 1977

MASON, 1986

F.M. Mason, 'The Newer Eve: The Catholic Women's Suffrage Society in England, 1911–1923', *Catholic Historical Review*, vol.lii, no.4, 1986

MCDONALD, 1989

I. McDonald, *Vindication! A Postcard History of the Women's Movement*, McDonald/Bellew, 1989

MITCHELL, D., 1965

D. Mitchell, *Women on the Warpath: The Story of Women in the First World War*, Jonathan Cape, 1965

MITCHELL, D., 1967

D. Mitchell, *The Fighting Pankhursts*, Jonathan Cape, 1967

MITCHELL, D., 1977

D. Mitchell, *Queen Christabel*, Macdonald, 1977

MITCHELL, G., 1968

G. Mitchell (ed.), *The Hard Way Up: The Autobiography of Hannah Mitchell*, 1968, reprinted Virago, 1984

MOORE, 1982

L. Moore, 'Feminists and Feminity: A Case Study of WSPU Propaganda and Local Response at the Scottish By-Election', *Women's Studies International Forum*, vol.v, no.6, 1982

MORGAN, 1975

D. Morgan, *Suffragists and Liberals: The Politics of Women's Suffrage in England*, Blackwell, 1975

MORLEY, 1988

A. Morley (with L. Stanley), *The Life and Death of Emily Wilding Davison*, Women's Press, 1988

MORRELL, 1981

C. Morrell, *'Black Friday': Violence against Women in the Suffrage Movement*, Women's Research and Resources Centre, 1981

MULVIHILL, 1989

M. Mulvihill, *Charlotte Despard: A Biography*, Pandora, 1989

MURPHY, 1989

C. Murphy, *The Women's Suffrage Movement and Irish Society in the Early Twentieth Century*, Harvester, 1989

NIELD CHEW, 1982

D. Nield Chew, *Ada Nield Chew: The Life and Times of a Working Woman*, Virago, 1982

OAKLEY, 1983

A. Oakley, 'Millicent Garrett Fawcett: Duty and Determination', in *Feminist Theorists*, ed. D. Spencer, Women's Press, 1983

OWENS CULLEN, 1984

R. Owens Cullen, *Smashing Times: A History of the Irish Women's Suffrage Movement, 1889–1922*, Attic Press, 1984

PAGE, 1987

K. Page, *The Unborn Dreams of Clara Riley*, Virago, 1987

PANKHURST, C., 1959

C. Pankhurst, *Unshackled: The Story of How We Won the Vote*, Hutchinson, 1959

PANKHURST, E., 1979

E. Pankhurst, *My Own Story: The Autobiography of Emmeline Pankhurst*, 1914, reprinted Virago, 1979

PANKHURST, R., 1979

R. Pankhurst, *Sylvia Pankhurst: Artist and Crusader*, Paddington Press, 1979

PANKHURST, S., 1911

S. Pankhurst, *The Suffragette*, Gay & Hancock, 1911

PANKHURST, S., 1977

S. Pankhurst, *The Suffragette Movement*, 1931, reprinted Virago, 1977

PARKER HUME, 1982

L. Parker Hume, *The National Union of Women's Suffrage Societies, 1897–1919*, Garland Publishing, New York, 1982

POLLOCK, 1989

C.R. Pollock, 'Against the Tide: The Anti-War Arguments of British Suffragists during the First World War' (thesis), Calgary, Alberta, 1989

PUGH, 1980

M.D. Pugh, *Women's Suffrage in Britain, 1867–1928*, Historical Association, 1980

RAEBURN, 1973

A. Raeburn, *The Militant Suffragettes*, Michael Joseph, 1973

RAMELSON, 1967

M. Ramelson, *The Petticoat Rebellion*, Lawrence & Wishart, 1967

RIEMER & ROUT, 1980

E. Riemer and J. Rout, *European Women: A Documentary History 1789–1945*, Harvester Press, 1980

ROLFE, 1979

D. Rolfe, 'Origins of Mr Speaker's Conference during the First World War', *History*, vol.lxiv, 1979

ROLLEY, 1990

K. Rolley, 'Fashion, Feminity and the Fight for the Vote', *Art History*,
vol.xiii, no.1, 1990

ROMERO, 1987

P.W. Romero, *E. Sylvia Pankhurst: Portrait of a Radical*, Yale, 1987

ROSEN, 1974

A. Rosen, *Rise Up Women: The Militant Campaign of the WSPU 1903–14*,
Routledge & Kegan Paul, 1974

ROVER, 1967

C. Rover, *Women's Suffrage and Party Politics in Britain, 1866–1919*,
Routledge & Kegan Paul, 1967

ROWBOTHAM, 1973

S. Rowbotham, *Hidden from History*, Pluto Press, 1973

RUBINSTEN, 1986

D. Rubinsten, *Before the Suffragettes: Women's Emancipation in the 1890s*,
Harvester Press, 1986

SARAH, 1982

E. Sarah, 'Female Performers on a Male Stage', in *On the Problem of Men*,
eds S. Friedman and E. Sarah, Women's Press, 1982

SARAH, 1983

E. Sarah, 'Christabel Pankhurst: Reclaiming her Power', in *Feminist
Theorists*, ed. D. Spender, Women's Press, 1983

SOLOMAN, 1991

M. Soloman (ed.), *A Voice of Their Own: The Woman Suffrage Press
1840–1910*, University of Alabama Press, 1991

STOCKS, 1949

M.D. Stocks, *Eleanor Rathbone*, Gollancz, 1949

STOWELL, 1992

S. Stowell, *A Stage of Their Own: Feminist Playwrights of the Suffrage Era*,
Manchester University Press, 1992

STRACHEY, 1931

R. Strachey, *Millicent Garrett Fawcett*, John Murray, 1931

STRACHEY, 1931

R. Strachey, *The Cause: A Short History of the Women's Movement in Great
Britain*, 1931, reprinted Virago, 1978

SWANWICK, 1935

H.M. Swanwick, *I Have Been Young*, Gollancz, 1935

TICKNER, 1988

L. Tickner, *The Spectacle of Women: Imagery of the Suffrage Campaign,
1907–14*, Chatto, 1988

TREMAIN, 1973

R. Tremain, *The Fight for Freedom for Women*, Ballantine, 1973

VELLACOTT, 1987

J. Vellacott, 'Feminists' Consciousness and the First World War',
History Workshop, no.23, Spring 1987

VELLACOTT NEWBERRY, 1977

J. Vellacott Newberry, 'Anti-War Suffragists', *History*, vol.lxii, 1977

VICINUS, 1972

M. Vicinus (ed.), *Suffer and Be Still: Women in the Victorian Age*, Methuen,
1972

VICINUS, 1972

M. Vicinus (ed.), *The Widening Sphere: Changing Roles of Victorian Women*,
Methuen, 1972

WELLS, 1909

H.G. Wells, *Ann Veronica*, 1909, reprinted Virago, 1980

WILTSHER, 1985

A. Wiltsher, *Most Dangerous Women: Feminist Peace Campaigners of the
Great War*, Pandora, 1985

WOLLSTONECRAFT, 1792

M. Wollstonecraft, *Vindication of the Rights of Women*, 1792, reprinted
Penguin, 1982

WRIGHT, 1913

Sir A.E. Wright, *The Unexpurgated Case against Woman Suffrage*,
Constable, 1913

AT LAST!

INDEX

Page numbers in *italics* refer to illustrations
References to numbers in the List of Exhibits are in **bold** following the page number

Actresses' Franchise League 55; banners *55*, 109(**550–1**), 110(**556**); colours 24, 119(**655**); musicians' section 110(**556**); publications 65–6(**65–72**)
Adkins, H.S. 62(**24**)
Ainslie, Kathleen 67(**85**)
Ainsworth, Laura *37, 37*, 78(**184**), 83(**233**)
Allinson's 25
Ansell, Gertrude Mary 106(**518**)
Anti-Suffrage Alphabet Book 11, 65(**60**)
Artists' Suffrage League 55; publications 73(**134**)
'Ask With Courage' banner *23*, 118(**650**)
Auld, C. 94(**370**)
Ayrton, Barbara *40*, 75(**155**)

badges *30*, *31*, *32*, *40*, *55*, 79(**194–5, 199, 201–2**), 80(**209**), 90(**319–21**), 113(**599**); prison-related *37*, 105–6(**507–9**); *see also* rosettes
bags 26, *36*, 105(**503**)
Baines, Jennie 64(**50**), 81(**215**), 94(**365**), 106(**511**)
Baldock, Minnie 84(**258**), 92(**349**), 97–8(**407–8**), 104(**497**)
Balls, Norah *19*
bands; men's 94(**371**), 102(**463**); women's 27, 57, 77(**178**), 81(**222**), 101(**455**)
banners *40*, 88(**300–1**), 109(**551**), 117(**635–42**), 118–19(**644–53, 656**); 'Ask With Courage' *23*, 118(**650**); 'Boadicea' *54*; Chelsea *42*, 118(**651**); Hammersmith *6*, 119(**652**); 'Holloway Prisoners' 119(**656**); West Ham *22*, 118(**647**)
Bartels, Mary *47*, 83(**236**)
Beaconsfield Laundry 26
bell 70(**114**)
Bell, Annie 26
belts *36, 40*; buckles 79(**198**)

Bennett, P.R. 66(**70**)
Bensusan, Inez 66(**71**)
Besant, Annie 7
bicycles 27
'Black Friday' 108–9(**544–6**)
Blease, W. Lyon 104(**492**)
Boadicea, imagery of *54*, 117(**639**), 118(**644**)
books *11, 31, 32*, 65(**60**), 67(**84**), 97(**403**), 104(**490**), 114–15(**612–18, 620–2**)
Brailsford, H.N. 108(**541**)
breakfast parties 104(**496–7**), 106(**517**), 107(**521**), 107(**532**)
Bright, Florence 63(**30**)
brooches *31, 55*, 79(**197**), 105(**500**); battery-operated 25; Holloway 83(**233**)
Brough, Fanny 34
Bryce, Annan 76(**167**), 109(**553**)
Buckingham Palace 114(**607–9**)
bus, suffragette *40*
businesses, support for WSPU 19–21, 25–7; during most militant campaigning 28–9
buttons *18*, 80(**205**)

cakes 27, 31
calendars 31, 80(**214**)
Calling All Women 115(**624–5**)
Capper, Mabel 75(**156**), 81(**215**)
cards see games, greetings cards *and* postcards
Carlyle, Thomas 111(**568**)
cars *37*
'Cat and Mouse Act' *42*, 106(**518**), 107(**528**), 108(**535**)
catapult 111(**575**)
census, 1911, opposition to 95(**373–4**)
Central Society for Women's Suffrage 63(**38**)
chains 93(**361–2**), 119(**653**)
Chappelon, Grace 75(**154**)
Chelsea WSPU *42*, 118(**651**)
china *50*, 80(**211**)

chocolates 27, 48

Cholmeley, Robert F. 63(**29**), 113(**597**)

Christmas Bazaar 56, 76(**162–4**)

Christmas cards 26–7, 31, 81(**219, 222**), 82(**224**), 83(**235**)

cigarettes 48

Clayton, Margaret S. 63(**32**)

Cobbe, Frances Power 62(**26**)

colours, suffragette 14–25, 57; origin and symbolism 15; other organisations and 24, 54

Cooke, Florence E. 106(**514**)

cookery book 97(**403**)

Coombes, Mrs 98(**408**)

Corbet, Mrs Frank 93(**356**)

Corelli, Marie 67(**87**)

Coronation Procession, Women's 25, 26, 76(**167**), 109–10(**547–63**); handbills, etc., for 26, 109(**547–8**); programme 109(**549**)

cosh 111(**577**)

Courtauld, Catherine 62(**25**), 71–2(**122–4**), 73(**128, 132**); 'Ostrich' 71(**122**), 88(**305**); 'The Prehistoric Argument' 73(**132**), 116(**631**); 'Waiting for a Living Wage' 62(**25**), 89(**308**)

crackers 31

Curie, Marie, banner about 88(**301**), 117(**641**)

Dallas, Hilda 101(**458**); designs by 4, 26, 46, 83(**235, 238**), 114(**607**)

Davies, Emily 63(**38**)

Davison, Emily Wilding 84(**252**), 95–6(**375–92**); funeral and memorials 95–6(**381–5, 388–92**); items used, etc., by 95(**377**), 96(**387**), 117(**643**)

Debenham and Freebody 29

decorating, house 26

Derry and Toms 20, 21

Despard, Charlotte 84(**254**)

dolls 31

Douglas Smith, Miss 40, 91(**327**)

Downing, Edith 25

Dowson, Mrs Aubrey 97(**403**)

Drew, Joan Harvey 71(**119**)

Drummond, 'General' Flora 41, 41, 44, 77(**173**), 84(**251**), 90(**324**), 91(**329**), 93(**351**), 94(**370**), 97(**396, 404, 407**), 100(**445**), 101(**450**), 103(**481–2**), 107(**530**); items presented to 90(**316–18**); letter signed by 92(**344**); office 40

du Cros, Arthur 111(**573**)

Dugdale, Daisy 22, 101(**454, 456**)

Dugdale, Una 96(**394**)

Dunhill cigarettes 29

Dutton, Frederic G. 69(**110**), 73(**131**)

Duval, Victor 112(**587**)

Earengey, W.G. 63(**35**)

East, Mrs 30

Eckford, Dorothy 25

Elswick Cycle Company 27

Englishwoman, The 63(**29**)

epaulettes 90(**318**)

Esperanto 61(**13**)

Evans, D.H. 29

Evans, Gladys 102(**462**)

Exhibition, The Women's see Women's Exhibition

Express Dairy 29

'Factory Acts' poster 10, 116(**632**)

fashion, politics and 15, 19–21, 25

Fawcett, Millicent Garrett 8, 24

feathers 10, 83(**243**)

Fergus, Olive 93(**356**)

flags 31, 117(**643**), 119(**654–5**)

Flatman, Ada 60(**2**), 85(**266**), 94(**370**), 107(**524**)

flowers 18

force-feeding 104(**486, 489, 493–5**), 105(**506**), 107(**529**), 108(**534**), 116(**633**)

Ford, Emily 10, 116(**632**)

Franklin, Hugh A. 112(**589**)

games 30–1, 31, 36, 36, 38, 43, 86(**276–7, 280, 282**); see also playing cards

Gatty, Katharine 103(**479**)

Gawthorpe, Mary 21, 75(**156**), 85(**264, 273**), 104(**496**)

Gibbons sisters 27

Glover, Evelyn 65(**65**), 66(**72**)

Great Scourge, The 63(**33**)

greetings cards 81 (**220, 223**), 83(**234**); see also Christmas cards

Greig, Theresa Billington 84(**256**)

Gye, Elsa 91(**327**), 94(**370**), 108(**537**)

Haig, Florence 105(**506**)
Hamilton, Cicely 66(**75**), 73(**134**)
Hammersmith WSPU 6, *6*, 65(**56**), 119(**652**)
handbills *32, 45*, 60(**3**), 64–5(**45–58**), 67(**82**), 73(**133**),
    77(**175**), 86(**287**), 87(**290**), 92(**347**), 98–9(**411–14**,
    419, 421–3, 425, 428, 431–2, 434), 104(**493, 495**),
    106(**514–15**), 107(**528–9**), 109(**547–8**), 110(**564–5**),
    114(**607**)
handkerchief case 105(**504**)
handkerchiefs *15*, 82(**230–1**); paper 86(**283–4**)
Hardie, James Keir 113(**602**); Flora Drummond and 41
Harding Andrews, Emily J. 61(**12**)
harness 93(**362**)
Harraden, Beatrice 65(**64**)
Hartley-Wilson, E. 70(**115**)
Harvey Nichols 29
hatpins see pins
hats 25, 26, 90(**316**)
'Haunted House' design 79(**198**), 89(**310**)
Hedley-Charlton, C. 73(**134**)
Holloway Prison 22, 93–4(**363–4**), 103(**473–5, 477–8,
    483–5**); items from 104(**498**), 105(**501, 505**); items
    made in *11*, 105(**499, 502, 504**); items related to *37*,
    83(**233**), 117(**640**); letters from 107(**524**); releases
    from 92–3(**349–51**), 94(**365**), 101(**453–4, 456–7**),
    102(**461**), 106(**510**), 107(**522–3, 531**), 108(**533**) (see
    also breakfast parties); rules 106(**512**)
Holme, Vera 'Jack' *37*, 84(**259**), 93(**360**)
Holmes, Marion 63(**39**)
Home Restaurant 25
Housman, Clemence 71(**121**)
Housman, Laurence *11*, 65(**60**), 66(**76**), 95(**374**),
    113(**603**)
How-Martyn, Edith 84(**255**)
Howey, Elsie 76(**165**), 84(**260**), 102(**464**)
Hughes, M. 62(**18**)
hunger-strikes 102(**462**), 119(**656**); medals *37*, 83(**233**),
    103(**480**), 105(**506**)
Hutchins, B.L. 64(**42**)

Irishwomen's Suffrage Federation 67(**83**)

Jacobs, Louise 89(**307**), 116(**629**)
Jaeger 21, 29
jam 31
Jay, Annette 26
Jennay, Revd Marie 64(**46**)
Jennings, Gertrude 66(**67**)
jewellery 31; *see also* brooches *and* necklaces
Joachim, Miss 94(**370**)
Joan of Arc, imagery of 46, 76(**165, 167**), 83(**234, 238**),
    87(**298–9**), 102(**464**), 109(**553**), 114(**611**)
John, N.A. 104(**491**)
Johnston, Thomas 64(**41**)
Jones, Grace 26

Keegan, Miss 94(**370**)
Keevil, Gladice 93(**358**)
Kelly, Miss *40*, 75(**151**), 94(**370**)
Kenney family 43
Kenney, Annie *21*, 43, *43*, 44, 84(**261**), 85(**273**),
    91(**333**), 92(**349**), 104(**496, 497**), 114(**612**), 119(**656**);
    statuettes of 25
Kenney, Jessie 13, *13, 21*, 84(**263**), 85(**273**); office
    74(**145**)
Kensington WSPU 31, 33
Knight, Mrs 34

Lamb, Aeta 91(**327**)
Lansbury, George 112(**590**)
Larkcom, Agnes 119(**655**)
lectures 98(**418**)
Leigh, Mary 57, 77(**178**), 81(**215**), 84(**257**), 92(**349**),
    101(**453**), 102(**462**), 106(**520**), 107(**524**), 108(**533**),
    111(**567**)
Leo, Rosa 26
letters 92(**343–4**), 107(**524**); 'human' 93(**352–3**)
Liberty's 19
Lilley and Skinner 21
lingerie 21, 26
Lloyd George, David 112(**583**)
London National Society for Women's Suffrage 62(**26**)
London Shoe Company 21
Lowndes, Mary 55; designs and banners by *54*, 62(**21**),
    73(**134**), 88(**300–1**), 117(**636, 639–41**), 118(**644–5**,
    649); pamphlet by 117(**638**)

Lytton, Lady Constance 85(**270**), 103(**480**), 109(**555**), 115(**621**)

Lytton, Earl of 113(**601**)

'MaC' 61(**16**), 62(**19**)

Macfadyen, Irene M. Ashby 60(**5**)

McGill, Donald 68(**94**)

McLaren, Lady 63(**28**)

Malmberg, Aino 60(**8**)

'March of the Women, The' 65(**63**), 66(**74**)

Margesson, Miss 33

Marsh, Charlotte 76(**166**), 101(**458**), 115(**619**)

Marshall and Snelgrove 29

Martel, Nellie Alma 60(**2, 4**), 85(**265**), 97(**401**), 104(**497**)

medals 37, 83(**233**), 103(**480**), 105(**506**)

Meeson-Coates, D. 73(**134**)

Men's League for Women's Suffrage 11, 113(**599–600, 604–5**); *Monthly Paper* 112(**592–4**)

Men's Political Union for Women's Enfranchisement 112(**587, 589, 591**)

Mill, John Stuart 112(**586**), 113(**595**)

Mills, Ernestine 71(**118**), 72(**125**)

Mills, Roberta 25, 26

Mitchell, Hannah 114(**614**)

Moore, Ada 119(**655**)

Moreland, Arthur 68(**95, 97–8**)

Morris, Margaret 65(**63**)

Moullin, Mrs Mansell 85(**267**)

music *17*; *see also* songs

musicians 110(**556**); *see also* bands

National Union of Women's Suffrage Societies 8; colours 24; publications 60(**10**), 63(**34, 40**)

necklaces *35, 39*, 79–80(**203–4**), 101(**451**)

New, Edith 101(**453**), 106(**520**), 108(**533**), 111(**567**)

newspapers *see individual titles*

Oliver, Mrs 20

Palmer, Frank 63(**32**)

pamphlets 60(**4–10**), 62–4(**26–32, 34–44**), 67(**81, 83, 85–7**), 73(**134**), 86(**288**), 96(**386**), 104(**488–9, 491–2, 494**), 106(**513, 516**), 108(**534, 541, 543**), 113(**597–8,**

601–4, **606**), 115(**619, 623**), 117(**638**)

'Pank-a-Squith' (game) *30, 31,* 86(**282**)

Pankhurst family 7, 9, 12–13

Pankhurst, Adela 8, *8*, 84(**262**), 97(**401**), 104(**496**), 111(**574**), 115(**616**)

Pankhurst, Christabel 7, 9, *9*, 12–13, *21*, 27, 29, 44–7, 84(**247**), 85(**273**), 90(**325**), 91(**329, 333**), 100(**445**), 101(**450**), 103(**475, 481–2**), 104(**496–7**), 107(**521, 530, 532**), 110(**565**); handbills by 64(**51, 53**), 65(**55**); imprisonments/releases from prison 22, 23, 93(**351**), 101(**453, 456–7**); items using image etc. 25, 26, 27, 36, 86(**278**), 106(**519**), 116(**628**), 119(**656**); modelled at Madame Tussaud's 85(**271**); pamphlet by 64(**43**); postcard sent to 70(**112**)

Pankhurst, Emmeline 7, 8, *8*, 12–13, 37, 44–7, 84(**246**), 85(**274**), 91(**333**), 97(**396, 401**), 100(**445**), 101(**450–1**), 103(**475, 481–2**), 104(**496**), 107(**521, 528, 530, 532**), 114(**615**), 117(**642**); collar embroidered by *10*, 84(**245**); imprisonments/releases from prison 22, 23, 27, 93(**351**), 94(**364, 369**), 101(**453, 456–7**); items used, worn, etc., by *10, 39*, 65(**63**), 80(**204**), 83(**243–4**), 108(**535**); items using image etc. *11*, 26, 32, 36, 79(**194**), 80(**208–9**), 83(**242**), 106(**519**), 119(**656**); pamphlet by 64(**44**); resolution signed by 94(**366**)

Pankhurst, Richard 7

Pankhurst, Sylvia 7, 9, *9*, 52, 84(**248**), 85(**272**), 104(**496**), 114(**613**); designs by 27, 31, 52, *56*, 108(**537**), 114(**613**), ('angel') 22, *50*, 52, 80(**211**), 81(**216**), 87(**294**), 99(**428**), 118(**647**), (convict's arrow) 105(**500**), ('seeds') *51*, 80(**212, 214**), 81(**218–19**), 87(**295–7**), 99(**424, 435**), (woman stepping over chains) *55*, 79(**199**), 82(**224, 227–8**), 115(**621**); mural for Women's Exhibition 77(**170**)

'Panko' (game) *30–1*, 31, *36,* 86(**276**)

Paul, Alice 54, 60(**1**)

Paull, H.M. 66(**69**)

Pearse, Alfred *46*, 61(**15**), 88(**302**), 116(**633**)

Penny, Thomas 67(**90**)

Pertwee, Emily 119(**655**)

Peter Robinson 19, 20

Pethick, Dorothy *21*, 85(**273**)

Pethick-Lawrence, Emmeline 12–13, *12, 21*, 37, 44–7, 54, 84(**250**), 85(**273**), 90(**325**), 91(**329, 335**), 104(**496**), 115(**618**), 119(**656**); handbill by 65(**54**); items using

image etc. 36; office 75(**149**); and suffragette
  colours 14, 15, 16
Pethick-Lawrence, Frederick 12–13, *12*, 31, 44–7,
  64(**48**), 84(**249**), 106(**515**), 115(**617**)
Phelps, Elspeth 20
Phibbs, Mrs Harlow 66(**68**)
Phillips, Mary *41*, 75(**157**), 102(**461**), 106(**510**),
  107(**531**)
photographers 26
pins *30*, 31, *55*, 79(**196**, **200**)
Piper, George 69(**104**)
playing cards *35*, 36, 86(**286**)
plays 55, 65–6(**64–73**, **75–6**)
Pocock, Isabel 71(**117**)
police 92(**384**), 100–1(**444–50**), 102(**471**), 109(**545–6**),
  111(**570**), 114(**608**); charge sheets 107(**526**)
'Polling Station' poster 6, 88(**306**)
postcards 61–2(**13–25**), 63(**33**), 67–73(**88–113**, **115–32**),
  74–5(**136–54**), 76(**162–3**, **165**), 77(**169–74**), 78–9
  (**181–93**), 81(**216**, **218–19**, **221–2**), 82(**224–6**, **229**),
  83(**233**), 84–5(**246–69**, **273–5**), 87(**289**), 90–1(**323–7**),
  92(**342**), 94(**370–1**), 95(**375**, **380**, **383**), 96(**388**, **391**),
  97(**396–402**), 98(**420**), 101(**448–9**), 102(**459**),
  103(**473**, **476**, **479–80**, **482**), 104(**486**), 107(**532**),
  108(**535**, **540**), 109(**552–3**), 110(**560**, **563**), 112(**584**,
  586–91), 114(**611**); albums 31, 82(**227–8**)
posters 4, 40, 61(**12**), 83(**236–41**), 88–9(**302–11**), 115–
  16(**626–34**); 'Cat and Mouse' 42, 83(**239**); 'Factory
  Acts' *10*, 116(**632**); 'Polling Station' 6, 88(**306**)
Potts, Reginald *17*, 82(**229**)
Powell, K.F. 62(**22**)
'press carts' 37, *37–8*, 75(**150**), 76(**161**), 78(**186**)
prisons 102(**462**); imagery of 79(**200**), 85(**266**), 86(**286**),
  92(**350**), 93–4(**355**, **359**, **363–5**, **367–71**), 102(**472**),
  103(**475–9**), 105(**500**, **503**), 109(**552**), 118(**648**); see
  also Holloway Prison
programmes 65(**59**), 76(**164**), 98(**416–17**), 99(**424**, **426**,
  430, **436**), 100(**438**, **442**), 106(**517**), 107(**527**),
  109(**549**)
public-speaking classes 26
'Purple, White and Green March, The' *17*, 82(**229**)

Radcliffe, Dorothy 101(**458**), 102(**460**)
receptions 65(**59**), 99(**435**)

Reed, E.T. *see* 'Panko'
resolutions 94(**366**)
ribbons 90(**322**); *see also* sashes *and under* rosettes
Richardson, Mary 111(**569**), 115(**622**)
Robins, Elizabeth 63(**31**)
Robinson and Cleaver 28
Robson, Ruth 22
Roe, Grace 85(**269**), 101(**448**)
rosettes *14*, 80(**206**, **210**); ribbons *15*, 80(**206–8**, **210**)
Ross, Herman 42, 118(**651**)
Royden, A. Maude 63(**34**, **40**)

St Ivel 27
St John, Christopher (Christabel Marshal) 66(**75**)
sashes 23, 89–90(**312–15**, **317**)
scarves *14*, 31, 36, 82(**232**)
scroll 108(**537**)
sculptures *11*, 83(**242**), 105(**499**)
self-defence 26
'Self-Denial Weeks' 54, *57*, 86–7(**288–9**, **291**)
Selfridge's 27, 28
Sennett, Mrs Arncliffe 107(**525**), 117(**636**)
shackles 93(**361–2**)
Sharp, Evelyn 34
Shaw, George Bernard 57, 67(**83**)
shoes *10*, 21, 83(**344**)
Simon, E.M. 67(**86**)
Sinclair, Herbert 66(**80**)
Slee, Mary 82(**226**)
Smith, Lady Sybil 63(**36**)
Smyth, Ethel 65(**63**), 66(**74**)
Snowden, Philip 112(**588**)
Snowden, Mrs Philip 60(**6**)
soap 25, *51*, 80(**212**)
socks 105(**502**)
songs 65(**61–3**), 66(**74**, **77–80**), 82(**229**)
Sproson, Emma 93(**357**), 97(**406**)
stationery 31, 36, 48, 86(**281**, **285**)
Stetson, C.P. 72(**125**)
Stout, Lady 60(**3**)
Strong, Clara 25
Suffrage Annual and Women's Who's Who 28, 81(**217**)
Suffragette, The 28, 29, 44–7, 49, 56, 76(**168**), 104(**487**),
  108(**536**); advertising in 28, 29, 48; circulation 48;

posters advertising 46–7, 83(**236**, **238–9**) ; selling 48, 49, 63(**33**), 75(**153**, **158–9**)

suffragette bus 40

'Suffragette, The Game of' 31, 43, 86(**277**)

Suffragette Fellowship 10, 115(**619**, **624–5**)

Suffragette Self-Defence Club 26

suffragettes: origin of name 9; colours see colours; see also Women's Social and Political Union

'Suffragettes In and Out of Prison' (game) 38, 86(**280**)

Swan and Edgar 29

tablecloths 86(**279**)

tea 27, 40, 48

teasets 31, 50, 80(**211**)

telegrams 107(**525**)

Terrero, Jane 105(**505**), 107(**526**)

Thompson-Price, L. 71(**126–7**)

tickets 91(**328**), 98(**415**, **418**), 99(**427**, **433**, **435**), 100(**437**, **440–1**, **443**)

ties 31, 40, 80(**213**)

toys 86(**278**) ; see also games

Tuckwell, Mrs 37

Tuke, Mabel 84(**253**)

Tyson, Diana Katrina 105(**508**)

Tyson, Helena 105(**507**)

Tyson, Leonora 106(**509**)

underwear 21, 26

USA 54

Vicary, Charles Lane 71(**116**)

'Victoria Queen and Mother' banner 117(**636**), 118(**649**)

Votes For Women newspaper 15, 18, 20, 24–9, 31, 33, 34, 39, 58–9, 60(**11**), 92(**345**); advertising in 19, 25, 26, 27, 28; circulation 19; fashion feature 19–20; posters advertising 116(**628**); selling 37, 40–1, 58–9, 74(**147**), 75(**150–2**, **154**, **156–7**), 76(**160**), ('press carts') 37, 37–8, 75(**150**), 76(**161**), 78(**186**), (suffragette bus) 40; WSPU split and 44–7

Wallis, Mrs Courtenay 25

Ward-Higgs, W. 66(**77**)

Warton, Jane see Lytton, Lady Constance

Watson, Olive 101(**447**)

weddings 22

Wentworth, Vera 66(**66**), 85(**268**)

West Ham WSPU 22, 118(**647**)

Who's Who, Women's 28, 81(**217**)

Wilson, David 79(**198**), 89(**310**)

Wimbledon WSPU 65(**62**), 76(**162**)

Wollstonecraft, Mary 63(**32**)

Woman's Press, The 31–40, 44; annual reports and finances 34, 87(**292–9**); at Charing Cross Road 34–40, 34–5, 74(**147**), 78(**181–3**, **185–6**), (clock) 39; at Clement's Inn 31, 31, 34, 44, 44, 74(**137–41**, **143–6**), 75(**148–9**); at Lincoln's Inn House 44, 45, 74(**135–6**, **142**); other shops 78–9(**187–93**); political activities 29, 48; publications 60(**7**), 63(**36**), 64(**43–4**), 86(**288**), 104(**488**), 106(**516**), 108(**543**), 113(**601**), (handbills) 64–5(**45–50**, **52–4**, **57–8**), 106(**517**), 110(**564–5**), (programmes) 76(**164**), (songs) 65(**63**), 66(**74**); reduction in marketing work 29, 48; tea 27

Women Writers' Suffrage League 63(**31**), 65(**64**)

Women's Co-operative Guild 63(**37**)

Women's Exhibition, The 2–3, 52, 53, 77(**169–80**), 101(**455**); banners for 52, 77(**179**); catalogue 77(**169**, **176**); handbills for 51, 77(**175**, **177**); items in 50

Women's Freedom League: colours 24; publications 60(**8**), 63(**35**, **39**), 95(**374**), 113(**598**)

Women's Industrial Council 64(**42**)

Women's Parliament 98(**415**)

Women's Peace Army 115(**616**)

Women's Social and Political Union 7, 51–7; aims 11; at Clement's Inn 12, 44, 44, 74(**137–41**, **143–6**), 75(**148–9**), 100(**445–6**), 101(**450**); at Lincoln's Inn House 44, 45, 74(**135–6**, **142**), 111(**570**); bands 27, 57, 81(**222**); business support for see businesses; demonstrations etc. 16, 50, 85(**270**), 96–9(**394–7**, **399–401**, **407–9**, **422–3**), 100(**442**), 101(**452**), 102(**466–72**), 108(**538**, **542**), 117(**635**), (handbills etc. for) 65(**56**), 98–9(**411–14**, **420–1**, **425**, **428–9**, **431–2**, **434**), 100(**439**), (see also Coronation Procession and 'Women's Sunday'); finances 31, 52, 54; image 16; imagery 51–2 (see also colours); logos 52; meetings etc. 98(**411–14**, **416–18**, **420**), 99(**424–7**, **429–30**, **432–4**), 100(**439–41**, **443**), 101(**452**), 108(**544**);

membership 13, 43; merchandising/marketing 11, 13; motto 7; publications 63(**30**), (handbills) 65 (**55–7**), 73(**133**), 86(**287**), 87(**290**), (songs) 65(**61–2**), 66(**78**), (see also The Suffragette, Votes For Women and The Woman's Press); shops *33*, *49*, 97(**398**); splits 44–7; staff 41; tactics 9, 28–9, 44, 110–12(**564– 85**), (items related to) 93(**361–2**), 111–12(**575, 577– 8, 581–2**); 'uniform' 16–18, 19, *19*, *22*, 23–4, 31 (see also colours); volunteers 41

Women's Suffrage Annual 28, 81(**217**)

'Women's Sunday' 16–18, *17*, 90–2(**325–6, 328–9, 331, 333–8, 340–4, 346**), 102(**459, 465**); advertising for 90(**323–4**), 91(**330**), 92(**347**); banners for *16, 42*, 91–2(**332, 334–5, 338–40, 346**); handbills for 98(**419**); tickets 91(**328**)

Women's Tea Company 27

Woodcock, Patricia 107(**522–3**)

Woolan, Edith 27

working-class women 13, 29, 43

Wright, Alice Morgan *11*, 83(**242**), 115(**623**)

Wright, Almroth E. 67(**83–4**)

Yates, Rose Lamartine *23, 56*, 85(**275**)

Young Women's Christian Association 118(**646**)

Zangwill, Israel 91(**335**)

Zimmern, Alice 60(**9**)